YORK NOTE

General Editors: Professor A
of Stirling) & Professor Suheil Busनःu (
University of Beirut)

John Fowles

THE FRENCH LIEUTENANT'S WOMAN

Notes by Hilda Spear

MA (LONDON) PH D (LEICESTER) FIBA
Senior Lecturer in English, University of Dundee

LONGMAN
YORK PRESS

YORK PRESS
Immeuble Esseily, Place Riad Solh, Beirut.

LONGMAN GROUP UK LIMITED
Longman House, Burnt Mill, Harlow,
Essex CM20 2JE. England
Associated companies, branches and representatives
throughout the world

© Librairie du Liban 1988

First published 1988
Fifth impression 1992

ISBN 0-582-02093-X

Printed in Hong Kong
WC/05

Contents

Part 1
Introduction

JOHN FOWLES was born in March 1926, in the little Essex town of Leigh-on-Sea, a town which he himself described as 'dominated by conformism – the pursuit of respectability'*. A little over a month after his birth the General Strike began, and though it was short-lived it left behind a legacy of anger and frustration. Then, in October 1929, the economic bubble burst, and America and Europe found themselves in the midst of what came to be known as the Great Depression.

Fowles's father, a cigar importer, weathered the economic storm comfortably and was able to send his son to Bedford School, where the boy did well; he excelled intellectually and was good at sport, particularly cricket. Forced at first to accept the discipline of his seniors, he later became Head Boy. This experience gave him an insight into power and domination and the evils which accompany them; it instilled in him 'a violent hatred of leaders, organizers, bosses: of anyone who thinks it good to get or have arbitrary power over other people'†. The shadow of war hung over his school life, and when he left school he was called up into the Royal Marines where he served as a junior officer.

In 1947, the war and his military service over, Fowles went up to Oxford where he studied French at New College, completing his BA degree in 1950. The following year he spent in France as a *lecteur* in English at the University of Poitiers; whilst there he reinforced his interest in French literature, reading Jean Giradoux (1882–1944) and going through what he has called his 'Gide phase' (André Gide, 1869–1951). His interest in style and in the artistic processes of creation, as well as his slightly mocking flirtation with existentialism, with modernism, with structuralism and various other contemporary 'isms', owe a great deal to French influence from Flaubert to the present day.

Following his appointment at Poitiers, he went on to teach English at a boys' school in Greece and fell in love with the country. His second novel, *The Magus* (1966), is set on a Greek island; steeped in magic

*Autobiographical entry in *World Authors: 1950–1970*; quoted in *Current Biography 1977*, ed. Charles Moritz, H. W. Wilson Company, New York, 1977, p. 159.
†Quoted from *World Authors: 1950–1970* in *Current Biography 1977*, p. 160.

and myth, it is perhaps the only possible setting for the intricate and fantastic deceptions perpetrated upon the narrator, English schoolteacher Nicholas Urfe, by the 'Magus', Maurice Conchis.

In 1956 Fowles married Elizabeth Whitton. They settled for a while in London, where he taught in a girls' school and simultaneously experimented with writing fiction. His first novel, *The Collector*, was published in 1963 and was seen by many critics as a masterpiece. It is often difficult to live up to that kind of praise lavished on a first book, and his next book, *The Aristos: A Self-Portrait in Ideas* (1965), which veered away from fiction to offer a series of philosophical thoughts for the twentieth century, was less popular.

When he left teaching, Fowles, who has always disliked towns and ·people *en masse*, moved from London to Lyme Regis on the Dorset coast, where he felt more able to live his own private and secluded life. There, he is Curator of the little Philpot Museum and follows his own pursuits and interests, enjoying the natural surroundings, reading, writing and generally taking pleasure in remaining out of the limelight. It is in this part of England that *The French Lieutenant's Woman* is set. Published in 1969, this novel was an immediate success. It has been followed more recently by a book of poetry, *Poems* (1973), a book of stories, *The Ebony Tower* (1974), the text to accompany a book of photographs, *Shipwreck: Photographs by the Gibsons of Scilly* (1974), three novels, *Daniel Martin* (1977), *Mantissa* (1982) and *A Maggot* (1985), *A Short History of Lyme Regis* (1982) and a number of other non-fiction books. It is apparent from this list that Fowles is a prolific writer and one at home in diverse genres, though his principal interest is in the novel. His novels show considerable diversity, particularly of setting and technique, though all have a similarity in the extreme demands they make upon the reader. Following the publication of *The French Lieutenant's Woman*, he was presented with the PEN Silver Pen Award (1969) and the W. H. Smith Award (1970).

The French Lieutenant's Woman, though published in 1969, belongs to 1967 when it was written, exactly a hundred years after the overt action begins; moreover, the plot of 1867 is seen through the interpretations and perspectives of a hundred years later, and our twentieth-century judgments are reinforced by the duality of the presentation.

The year 1867 is central to the Victorian Age and can thus be seen as embodying the philosophies and moral values of that era. It was also the year in which Thomas Hardy (1840–1928) left London and returned to Dorset and, furthermore, the year in which he decided to abandon poetry for prose and began his first novel, *The Poor Man and the Lady*, which was never published and the manuscript of which has been lost or destroyed. It seems hardly likely to be purely fortuitous that *The French Lieutenant's Woman*, with its detailed references to

Hardy, was set in 1867; it may perhaps be seen as Fowles's *The Poor Woman and the Gentleman* in a kind of reversal of Hardy's title.

Fowles makes considerable use of the historical background of the period in which his novel is set. It was a significant period of social reform, 1867 being the year the Second Reform Bill was passed. This bill brought about household suffrage in the towns but did not enfranchise the poor labourers of the county constituencies. In Chapter 16 of his novel, nevertheless, Fowles points out that in the debate on the Bill (which was passed in March and therefore during the action of our story) John Stuart Mill (1806–73) tried to argue for equal rights for women at the ballot box; he goes on to claim that 30 March 1867 'is the point from which we can date the beginning of feminine emancipation'. *The French Lieutenant's Woman*, however, is more concerned with social than with political injustice: it draws our attention to the gulf between rich and poor, to the lot of women, to the male chauvinism which ensured that the laws of morality governing the actions of men were infinitely more liberal than those governing the actions of women; it shows us something of the lives of rich and poor, of the contrasting working and living conditions and of the indignities suffered, particularly by the women of the working classes.

The Victorian Age is commonly viewed as an age of prudery and of hypocrisy. We are simultaneously aware of the existence of the great thinkers, the great writers, the great politicians of the time and of the abject poverty portrayed by novelists such as Charles Dickens (1812–70). In addition to the novelists of the period, John Fowles makes particular use of a book entitled *Human Documents of the Victorian Golden Age* by E. Royston Pike, the timely publication of which in 1967 coincided with the writing of *The French Lieutenant's Woman*. It is almost essential reading for anyone who wishes to understand the novel, and in his list of 'Acknowledgments' Fowles recommends it 'to any reader who would like to know more of the reality behind my fiction'.

Another significant landmark was the publication in 1859 of Charles Darwin's (1809–82) *Origin of Species*, with its then revolutionary theory of evolution. Its implied rejection of the biblical Creation story in Genesis was a shock to traditional religious belief and a source of argument and dissension both among the intelligentsia and more widely. Fowles uses Darwin as a point of contact between Charles and Dr Grogan, both of whom are ardent Darwinians. It is, of course, appropriate that Charles should be an amateur geologist, for it was a geologist, Sir Charles Lyell (1797–1875), who earlier in the century had first challenged theological beliefs about the age of the earth with his *The Principles of Geology* (1830–3). We might observe, too, that Charles Smithson inherits his Christian name from these two great doubters. More significantly, perhaps, the geological and the Darwinian theories of the nineteenth century marked a point of no return. It was no longer possible to ignore the findings of science, and the task of theologians since has been to reconcile them with faith. (For further discussion of the books mentioned in this and the preceding paragraph, see Part 3 of these Notes.)

It is in this crucial period, when traditional beliefs were being overturned, that *The French Lieutenant's Woman* is set. Charles, Victorian though he is, is one of the 'New Men' of his age; Sarah, on the other hand, lacking Charles's education and knowledge, gives an intuitive response to events, coloured by the author's own twentieth-century perspective; she is wise before her time and she suffers for it, since she lives in a nineteenth-century world that has no conception of twentieth-century ideas about individual freedom and women's liberation.

The French Lieutenant's Woman is not an historical novel in the usual sense, for it is not contained within the chronological period in which it is set. Were it to be seen merely as an historical novel, many of the allusions and references and much of the language would be ana-chronistic. Fowles, however, deliberately introduces perceptions which do not belong to the period, engaging his reader in the creative process from the outset and insisting that author and readers may have twentieth-century sensibilities which are at odds with the Victorian plot.

The late 1960s, when the novel was in gestation, are significant mainly because they represent a time a century later than the story of the novel; this enables the author to indulge in the duality of action which makes us aware of the gulf between the lives of the Victorian characters and our own. This can be illustrated by the description of Charles as he sets out in Chapter 8 on one of his geological forays. The true historical novelist would simply have described his dress so that we saw him as a typical Victorian; Fowles, too, describes his dress, but puts it in a twentieth-century perspective, explaining to the reader that he 'would have made you smile' and going on to describe in detail his 'stout nailed boots and canvas gaiters', his 'breeches of heavy flannel', his 'tight and absurdly long coat', and his 'canvas wideawake hat'. The list of the contents of his rucksack which follows makes us wonder how Charles was ever able to carry such a load on his trips to the Undercliff. We view him as a Victorian, but we judge him in the light of our own contemporary knowledge and customs. He has become a slightly comic figure in our eyes because of the invitation to us to 'smile' and the use of such words as 'absurdly . . . ludicrous'. Yet, to the Victorians he would have been neither absurd nor ludicrous, but rather, simply conventional.

The main problems in *The French Lieutenant's Woman* lie not in the language itself, though the use of foreign words and phrases, particularly Latin, may be a stumbling block, but in the innumerable allusions and references drawn from diverse sources. In Part 2 of these Notes words which can be looked up in a good short dictionary, such as *The Concise Oxford Dictionary*, have not been explained but difficulties which might not easily be resolved by recourse to a dictionary are annotated. Further discussion of the text may be found in Parts 3 and 4.

A note on the text

The French Lieutenant's Woman was begun on 25 January and completed on 27 October 1967, taking nine months from conception to birth! It was published in hardback in 1969 by Jonathan Cape in Britain and by Little, Brown & Company in the United States. It has been reprinted several times and has also had several paperback publishings in both countries. A number of minor revisions were made for the American edition, particularly in the 'American' Chapter 59. The edition used in the preparation of these notes is the 1971 Cape reprint of the first edition, but since students may well be using different editions chapter references rather than page numbers are used here.

Part 2

Summaries
of THE FRENCH LIEUTENANT'S WOMAN

A general summary

This novel is a love story which leaves us troubled and bewildered. It takes place in Hardy country on the south coast at Lyme Bay. Although it is a Victorian novel, it is seen from a twentieth-century perspective; the characters are simultaneously part of the nineteenth-century world and the creatures of their author's invention. The action takes place in 1867, but its conception belongs to 1967.

The French Lieutenant's 'woman' is the heroine, Sarah Woodruff. Her male counterpart is not the French Lieutenant but the dilettante geologist, palaeontologist and follower of Darwin, Charles Smithson, who is engaged to Ernestina (Tina) Freeman. Other significant characters are Charles's uncle Sir Robert who, by marrying late in life and producing an heir, disinherits his nephew; Sam Farrow, Charles's manservant; Ernestina's father, and her Aunt Tranter; an Irish doctor called Grogan; Mrs Poulteney who, in the hope of earning herself some credit in heaven, takes Sarah Woodruff as her companion; Mrs Fairley, Mrs Poulteney's odious housekeeper; and finally, the enigmatic figure of the author himself.

Today we might well think that Charles Smithson and Ernestina Freeman were ill-suited to each other, but theirs would have been a perfectly acceptable Victorian marriage: a handsome, intelligent man, well-behaved, with prospects of a modest fortune and a title, and a vainly pretty young lady, the only child of her father and heiress to a massive fortune acquired through trade; moreover, they thought themselves to be in love, which would have been an added bonus.

Charles, however, almost by accident finds himself involved with Sarah Woodruff, an ex-governess, the 'wicked woman' of Lyme Regis, whose putative affair with the French Lieutenant has become the talk and the scandal of the neighbourhood. Through curiosity, and sympathy with her plight, Charles allows himself to be gradually ensnared by Sarah until at last he sleeps with her, only to discover that the stories that have circulated in the village are without foundation – she was a virgin!

After a terrible scene with Ernestina, in which she threatens him with legal action, he breaks his engagement to her; he now determines to find Sarah again and put matters right between them by offering her marriage. At this point Sarah disappears; Charles searches for her assiduously, even employing a detective agency to trace her, to no avail. To help him forget, he travels abroad, first on the Continent and then to America. At last, nearly two years later, news comes of Sarah; Charles returns to England and goes to visit her.

At this point the author, who had already attempted to end the story prematurely in Chapters 43 and 44 by proposing that Charles should not visit Sarah at her hotel but should instead return to Ernestina and marry her, intervenes again. He offers us two possible endings: first that Charles finds Sarah again, meets the child he had fathered and – of course, because it is a Victorian romance! – marries Sarah to live happily ever after; alternatively, Charles finds Sarah again, does not recognise the child he had fathered and – of course, because it is a story seen in the light of twentieth-century cynicism – the two quarrel and Charles leaves in anger, never to see Sarah again.

Detailed summaries

Chapter 1

It is March 1867, and on the quay at Lyme Regis a couple are walking. Seen through the eyes of a mysterious third figure, they are shown to be fashionably dressed and appear to be rather superior people, not belonging to Lyme itself. There is yet another person, dressed in black, standing completely still at the very end of the quay.

As the novel progresses we realise that the observer in this scene is the author himself. This short chapter deliberately evokes the atmosphere of a Hardy novel; it contains two of Hardy's favourite narrative devices: the depiction of lonely figures in a landscape, and the use of an observer to draw a picture which has more in common with visual than with narrative art. At the same time, the choice of Lyme Regis and the Cobb for the background of the story calls to mind Jane Austen's *Persuasion*, a book to which our author refers in the next chapter.

NOTES AND GLOSSARY:

The Cobb: the long harbour wall at Lyme

what familiarity breeds: that is, contempt (*old proverb*)

Piraeus . . . Athens: Piraeus is the seaport for Athens

Armada: the Spanish Armada set sail to attack Britain in 1588, but was destroyed in storms at sea

Monmouth: James Scott, Duke of Monmouth (1649–85), the illegitimate son of King Charles II; on the king's death in 1685, Monmouth, who had been banished from the country, landed with a small force at

	Lyme Regis. He was defeated and beheaded
Henry Moore:	(1898–1986) well-known English sculptor
Michelangelo:	(1475–1564) Italian painter and sculptor
dundrearies:	long side-whiskers

Chapter 2

This chapter takes us directly into the observed scene of the previous one. The two figures walking together are now introduced through their own conversation; Tina, the daughter of a very rich man whose wealth comes from the drapery trade, is engaged to Charles, grandson of a baronet and a dilettante scientist. Their conversation also introduces the third figure to us: she is known locally as Tragedy or, more vulgarly, as the French Lieutenant's Woman, and she works for old Mrs Poulteney.

The two approach the strange woman and Charles briefly addresses her; her only response is a penetrating look, but she says nothing, and Charles and Tina retrace their steps back along the Cobb.

It is apparent to the reader that Charles is intrigued by the encounter and that, despite his assertion to the contrary, he feels a sense of mystery and romance. Tina, on the other hand, wants nothing to do with the woman and hurries him away from the scene.

NOTES AND GLOSSARY:

Neptune:	Roman god of the sea
galant:	(*French*) gallant, showing chivalry
Mr Darwin:	Charles Darwin (1809–82), English naturalist who propounded the theory of evolution
Et voilà tout:	(*French*) and that's all
Certhidium portlandicum:	technical term for a particular kind of stone found near Portland
Jane Austen . . . *Persuasion*:	the English novelist Jane Austen (1775–1817) wrote *Persuasion* in 1815, and it was published posthumously in 1818. The incident in which Louisa Musgrove falls down the steps at the Cobb occurs in Chapter 12

Chapter 3

The story is now back in the mind of the observer (or author), who briefly outlines Charles's family history for us. We learn that Charles has a little money inherited from his extravagant father, but that his real hope of both fortune and title rests on his ageing, unmarried uncle. The chapter ends with an account of a discussion between Charles and his uncle about marriage. This discussion is more significant for both men than we realise at the time.

Fowles deliberately introduces a number of anachronisms into the narrative, showing us the mid-nineteenth century through the perspective of the mid-twentieth century.

NOTES AND GLOSSARY:

palaeontology: the study of life in the geological past

adagio: musical term meaning 'at a slow pace'

Chartists: those who supported the 'People's Charter' of 1838

German Jew . . . Hamburg: Karl Marx (1818–83), the father of international communism, was a German Jew. He settled in London in 1849 and wrote *Das Kapital* whilst working in the Reading Room of the British Museum

Almack's: Almack's Assembly Rooms in St James's in London were the home of a celebrated gaming-club

Thirty-nine Articles: the articles of religion to which a person taking orders in the Church of England has to assent

Oxford Movement: a movement towards High Church principles in the Church of England; it started in Oxford in the 1830s

propria terra: (*Latin*) own ground

voyant . . . s'assurer: (*French*) seeing too much to reject and too little to confirm

Huxley [*footnote*]: Thomas Henry Huxley (1825–95), English biologist

infra dig.: (*Latin*) colloquial for 'beneath one's dignity'; from Latin, *infra dignitatem*

Gladstone: William Ewart Gladstone (1809–98) was British Liberal Prime Minister in 1868–74, 1880–5 and 1892–4

Macaulay: Thomas Babington Macaulay (1800–59), British historian

Lyell: Sir Charles Lyell (1797–1875), a Scottish geologist, published *Principles of Geology* (1830–3); see Fowles's comments about him in Chapter 19

Disraeli: Benjamin Disraeli (1804–81) was British Conservative Prime Minster in 1852, 1858–9, 1868 and 1874–80

Byronic: George Gordon, sixth Baron Byron (1788–1824), was an English poet

Chapter 4

We are now introduced to Mrs Poulteney, a wealthy inhabitant of Lyme, whose housekeeper, Mrs Fairley, is as harsh and unkind as her mistress.

In the previous spring, Mrs Poulteney, fearing for her soul, had decided that she must do a charitable deed by taking as companion someone who had fallen on hard times; in the belief that he was helping Sarah, the local vicar had suggested Sarah's name to her. This chapter rehearses for our amusement the conversation between Mrs Poulteney and the vicar and shows us her hypocrisy.

NOTES AND GLOSSARY:

Regency house: a house in the style of architecture belonging to the Regency period (1810–20)

Stygian: associated with the Styx; in classical mythology it was the river over which the shades of the dead were ferried to Hades

Gestapo: secret police of the German Nazi regime

other, more Grecian, nickname: that is, Tragedy, which was 'Grecian' in that Melpomene, one of the nine Muses, presided over the art of Tragedy

Duke of Wellington: Arthur Wellesley, First Duke of Wellington (1769–1852); his distinguished army career culminated in victory over Napoleon at Waterloo in 1815

parable of the widow's mite: see the Bible, Mark 12:42 and Luke 21:2–4

de haut en bas: (*French*) from the heights to the depths

de bas en haut: (*French*) from the depths to the heights

Chapter 5

This chapter tells us about Ernestina's earlier life and explains why she is staying with her Aunt Tranter at Lyme. It also shows us a slightly un-Victorian side of Ernestina as, half-dressed, she admires herself in the mirror, and suddenly the thought of sexual intercourse comes into her mind.

There is a slight feeling here that the author is making fun of Ernestina and of Victorian conventions; certainly some of his descriptions appear to parody the attitudes commonly put forward in Victorian novels.

NOTES AND GLOSSARY:

Phiz: pseudonym of Hablot Knight Browne (1815–82), an etcher and water-colourist, best known as the illustrator of Dickens's *Pickwick Papers*

John Leech: (1817–64) English artist and cartoonist, best known for his cartoons in *Punch* and for his illustrations of Dickens's Christmas books

Becky Sharp: an unpleasant, scheming character in William Makepeace Thackeray's (1811–63) *Vanity Fair*

Prinny, George IV: (1762–1830); in 1810, owing to the madness of his father, George III, he became Prince Regent ('Prinny'). He succeeded to the throne in 1820

bouderies: (*French*) sulks

Harley Street: the street in London in which many distinguished medical consultants conduct their practices

Hitler . . . Poland: Adolf Hitler (1889–1945), German dictator, invaded Poland on 1 September 1939, an act which precipitated the Second World War

Juliet . . . nurse . . . Romeo: characters from Shakespeare's *Romeo and Juliet*

peignoir: (*French*) dressing-gown

Laocoön: in Greek legend Laocoön, a Trojan priest, was crushed to death by serpents as a punishment

Satyr-shaped [*footnote*]: a Satyr was a woodland god, representing lust

Freud [*footnote*]: Sigmund Freud (1856–1939), the Austrian founder of psychoanalysis

---

Chapter 6

The story now returns to Mrs Poulteney, and through her discussion with the vicar we learn something of Sarah Woodruff's life and background: during the time when she was governess in the family of Captain John Talbot, in the nearby village of Charmouth, a French ship had been wrecked offshore, and Captain Talbot had taken in one of the injured seamen, a lieutenant, whose leg had been crushed. When the Frenchman had recovered he went to Weymouth, in order to take a passage home, and Sarah followed him there, apparently lodging with her cousin until the lieutenant left for France; in Victorian times this alone would have been enough to damn a woman. Despite this, the kindly Mrs Talbot offered to take her back as governess, but Sarah refused. Sarah is, of course, the French Lieutenant's Woman whom Charles and Ernestina had met on the Cobb. The vicar explains that she appears to be suffering from melancholia. Mrs Poulteney agrees to interview Sarah and finally takes her on as companion.

NOTES AND GLOSSARY:

Tennyson's 'homes of silent prayer': Alfred, Lord Tennyson (1809–92), English poet; the quotation is from *In Memoriam*, XXXII

Treitschke: Heinrich von Treitschke (1834–96), German historian

Good Samaritan: from the biblical story of the Good Samaritan; see Luke 10:30–7

Patmos: island in the Aegean Sea where St John is reputed to have seen apocalyptic visions

Dies Irae: (*Latin*) the wrath of God

McLuhan: Herbert Marshall McLuhan (1911–80), a Canadian sociologist and literary critic who maintained that the invention of printing encouraged man to be self-centred and introspective and was thus destructive of cohesive society

---

Chapter 7

It is now a new day, and the story moves from Mrs Poulteney to Charles, as his servant Sam draws the curtains on a beautiful, bright Dorset day. Despite the attractions of the day, Sam is in a bad mood, and when he is cross-questioned by Charles it transpires that Aunt Tranter's pretty maid has been humiliating him. Charles recognises an incipient love affair and in his turn teases the younger man.

The scene in this chapter takes us back to the nineteenth century and to *The Pickwick Papers*. The pastoral scene which Charles views from his window resembles, perhaps, a picture from a Hardy novel, framed as it is by the window, a typical Hardyesque device. Sam, however, is not a figure from Hardy but a latter-day Sam Weller. Literary comparisons follow thick and fast: Sam is also likened to Don Quixote's Sancho Panza and, in the same sentence, Ernestina's name is linked with that of Dorothea, the heroine of George Eliot's *Middlemarch*.

NOTES AND GLOSSARY:

Proustian: Marcel Proust (1871–1922) was a French novelist, author of *A la recherche du temps perdu* (13 volumes, 1913–28), one of the most influential novels of the twentieth century

gaufer-stitched: an ornamental pattern stitched in lines across old country smocks

commons: food supply

Quod est demonstrandum: (*Latin*) which is to be proved; the Latin phrase, 'Quod erat demonstrandum', used to be placed at the end of geometrical or logical proofs when they were complete

Ergo: (*Latin*) therefore; well then

Cupid: Roman god of love

the immortal Weller: Sam Weller, Mr Pickwick's lively Cockney servant in Charles Dickens's (1812–70) *The Pickwick Papers* (1837)

Beau Brummel: George Bryan (Beau) Brummell (1778–1840), trend-setter in men's fashions in the early years of the nineteenth century

Sancho Panza: servant to Don Quixote in the novel of that name by Miguel de Cervantes (1547–1616)

Dorothea: heroine of George Eliot's novel *Middlemarch* (1871–2); see note to next chapter

Chapter 8

When Ernestina awakes that morning she feels unwell, and Aunt Tranter greets Charles, tells him that Ernestina is resting and suggests he returns later that day for afternoon tea. Not altogether sorry to have a day to himself, Charles commissions Sam to buy some flowers to deliver to Ernestina and suggests that he (Sam) might also buy flowers for Mary; he then gives him the day off.

Charles now decides to go on a geological expedition along the shore in search of specimens. He searches diligently and finds a very fine lias fragment which he determines to give as a present to Ernestina. It is only then that he realises that the whole morning has gone and he has moved much more slowly than he had expected. Though not cut off by the tide, he cannot return along the beach as he had intended and he has to follow a path up the cliffs to the woods.

Here we are invited to look at the story through twentieth-century eyes and to observe the differences in knowledge and outlook that have occurred in the past hundred years.

NOTES AND GLOSSARY:

blue lias: a blue limestone rock, rich in fossils

Mecca: that is, a place of pilgrimage; it is the holy place of Islam, and every devout Moslem tries to visit it at least once in his lifetime

Mary Anning: (1799–1847) was, indeed, a remarkable woman; orphaned at the age of eleven, she became a palaeontologist, though completely untrained. When she was only twelve she discovered the fossil skeleton of *Ichthyosaurus platyodon*, to which

Fowles refers, and which is now in the British Museum
anningii: in other words, is named after her
Isocrina: technical name for a kind of rock
Baedeker: popular name for guide books published by the German firm of Karl Baedeker
George Eliot [*footnote*]: (1819–80) pseudonym of Mary Ann Evans, English novelist
***The Voyage of the Beagle*:** that is, *Journal of Researches into the Geology and Natural History of the Various Countries Visited by H.M.S. 'Beagle'*, Charles Darwin's day-to-day account of his first scientific expedition (1831–6)
***The Origin of Species*:** the book in which Darwin posited the theory of evolution (1859)
oubliette: (*French*) secret dungeon
Linnaean *Scala Naturae*: Carl Linnaeus (Linné) (1707–78) was a Swedish botanist. His *Systema Naturae*, which sets out a system of classifying plants, was published in 1735
exempli gratia **Charles Smithson:** (*Latin*) that is, 'of which Charles Smithson is an example'

Chapter 9

At the opening of the novel Sarah Woodruff has been Mrs Poulteney's companion for over a year. Mrs Poulteney finds her companionship satisfying in many ways: Sarah has improved the domestic atmosphere by showing kindness and understanding to the other servants; she reads well and shows devotion during the household worship; she remembers old Mrs Poulteney's birthday and gives her an embroidered antimacassar; and finally, she quietly accepts the task of taking religious tracts around the neighbourhood. On the other hand, she annoys her employer by going out alone; her state of health is such that the doctor insists she is given every afternoon off; she is disconcertingly frank when visitors ask her questions; and lastly, she still seems attached to the French Lieutenant. The housekeeper, Mrs Fairley, is jealous of Sarah and goes out of her way to spy on her and make adverse reports on her activities. This chapter ends with the housekeeper complaining that Sarah has taken to walking alone on Ware Commons.

The revelation about Sarah's walks on Ware Commons recalls to us Charles's excursion and prepares us for the two to meet on the Commons.

NOTES AND GLOSSARY:

Mrs Sherwood:	Mary Martha Sherwood (1775–1851), a prolific writer, mainly of children's books
Walter Scott:	(1771–1832) Scottish novelist, poet and historian
Jane Austen:	see note to Chapter 2
Drake family:	Sir Francis Drake (1540–96) was born near Tavistock in Devon; he was instrumental in defeating the Spanish Armada (1588)
green sickness:	an anaemic disease, mainly afflicting young women
Brechtian:	Bertholt Brecht (1898–1956) was a German playwright and poet
***Lama, lama sabachthane me*:**	see the Bible, Matthew 27:46 and Mark 15:34; Christ's words from the Cross mean, 'My God, my God, why hast thou forsaken me?'
Blue Vinny:	(*dialect*), a blue-moulded Dorset cheese

Chapter 10

This chapter begins where the previous one left off – on Ware Commons; the description is lush, full of flowers and birds and romantic implications. Thus it is both a shock and not altogether unexpected when we find that it is Charles who is present on Ware Commons, trying to find his way back to Lyme after climbing the path up the cliff in Chapter 8. When he sees a figure lying asleep on a secluded ledge below him we are aware before he is that it must be Sarah. Whilst he stares at her, she awakes and jumps to her feet; he realises that he is committing an impropriety and, with a brief apology, he leaves her and goes on his way.

When Fowles comments at the end of this chapter that 'the whole Victorian Age was lost' we must understand that he means Charles's Victorian ideas of suitable marriages, of the place of women in society, of the correct behaviour between a young man of the upper class and a young lady of the lower class. It is a pointer, at an early stage in the novel, of its probable outcome.

NOTES AND GLOSSARY:

Renaissance:	the great revival of art and letters under the influence of classical models which took place in the fourteenth, fifteenth and sixteenth centuries
Botticelli:	Sandro Botticelli (1444–1510), a famous Renaissance artist from Florence
Ronsard:	Pierre de Ronsard (1524–85), a French Renaissance poet

Rousseau:	Jean Jacques Rousseau (1712–78), the French educationalist, philosopher and writer
Noble Savage:	an idea propounded by Rousseau that Man in his natural state is good; he has been corrupted by civilisation

Chapter 11

Whilst Charles is wandering on Ware Commons, Ernestina is spending a depressing morning at home, only slightly relieved by the bouquet of flowers he has sent her. She vents her annoyance on Mary, whom she suspects of flirting with Charles, and whom she resents anyway because of her beauty and vivacity.

The second half of the chapter describes the background of Ernestina's family and recounts the episodes leading up to her engagement to Charles. It shows Ernestina as both more intelligent and more cunning than the average young lady of her day.

NOTES AND GLOSSARY:

grisette:	(*French*) young flirtatious girl from the working classes
Occam's . . . razor:	the principle that abstractions must be proved to have a necessary relationship with known realities; named after the philosopher William Ockham or Occam (?1300–?49)
Waterloo:	the Battle of Waterloo was fought in 1815
Flora:	the goddess of flowers
soubrettes:	(*French*) lady's maids in musical comedy
Don Juan:	a legendary adventurer, made famous in English literature by Lord Byron's *Don Juan* (1819–24)
Lord Brabazon Vavasour Vere de Vere:	Tennyson chose the name 'Lady Clara Vere de Vere' for his poem of that title about a heartless member of the aristocracy
Early Cretaceous:	period when chalky strata were deposited

Chapter 12

The story returns to Charles walking on Ware Commons. Emerging from the wood, he comes upon a dairy where he buys a bowl of milk; he is about to go on his way when he sees Sarah come out of the wood and go towards Lyme. The dairyman describes her as a whore [hoer], which angers Charles, so he follows her, determined in some way to make amends for this insult. He overtakes her, but she rebuffs him and insists on going on alone.

Charles returns to Lyme and visits Ernestina, who asks him for a full account of how he spent his day. This he gives her, omitting, however, his encounter with Sarah Woodruff. Meanwhile, Sarah is reproved by Mrs Poulteney for walking on Ware Commons, which has an evil reputation in the district. The chapter ends with Sarah contemplating suicide but also with the author's assurance that she will not kill herself.

We see here how Charles is slowly becoming entangled with Sarah, though she herself appears to reject his advances.

NOTES AND GLOSSARY:

hoying: herding animals by calling to them

a Jeremiah: a miserable character; see the Bible, Jeremiah and Lamentations

*Noli me tangere***:** (*Latin*) Touch me not: Christ's words to Mary Magdalene after his resurrection; see the Bible, John 20:17

*déshabille***:** (*French*) not fully dressed

labour of Hercules: Hercules was ordered by the Oracle of Delphi to atone for his wrongdoing by serving Eurystheus for twelve years; during this time Eurystheus set him twelve difficult and arduous 'labours' to perform

Sodom and Gomorrah: evil cities which God destroyed; see the Bible, Genesis 13–19

*Anschluss***:** (*German*) union or connection

Coleridge: Samuel Taylor Coleridge (1772–1834), English romantic poet

Bosch-like: Hieronymus Bosch (?1460–1516), a Dutch painter of the macabre and grotesque

Chapter 13

In this short chapter the author considers the differing functions of the author in Victorian times and now. He insists that there are times when the characters appear to have a life of their own and act without their author's consent; he suggests that freedom from authorial control is essential but that his discussion of his own role in no way breaks the illusion. He finishes by declaring that he is merely a reporter of facts and sums up the significant facts of the episode on Ware Commons from Sarah's point of view.

Despite his assurances, this digression is slightly disturbing in the context of a Victorian novel and serves to underline the changes made in narrative technique during this century.

NOTES AND GLOSSARY:

Alain Robbe-Grillet: (1922–) French novelist in the forefront of the *nouveau roman* (new novel) movement; his narrative technique is unorthodox and revolutionary

Roland Barthes: (1915–80) French writer and critic, one of the originators of the critical movement known as 'structuralism'

Perhaps . . . puppets . . . manner: a reference to Thackeray's preface to *Vanity Fair* (1848)

hypocrite lecteur: (*French*) hypocritical reader; from Charles Baudelaire's (1821–67) *Les Fleurs du Mal*, quoted by T. S. Eliot (1888–1965) in *The Waste Land*

Homo sapiens: (*Latin*) sapiens = wise, but the phrase is used to distinguish man from his animal predecessors

Chapter 14

The story continues with an account of a morning visit to Mrs Poulteney made by Mrs Tranter and the engaged couple. Tensions are set up between various characters as the servants are discussed and Charles and Ernestina find themselves on opposite sides of the argument.

There are two brief but significant events: first, a moment of understanding between Sarah and Charles, and second, Charles's decision to teach Ernestina a lesson. The chapter ends with a serious conversation between Sam and Mary.

NOTES AND GLOSSARY:

Periclean oration: Pericles (*c.*490–429BC), Athenian statesman famed for his oratory

Mr Disraeli and Mr Gladstone: see notes to Chapter 3

Charles Darwin: see note to Chapter 2

Chapter 15

Charles and Tina make it up after their tiff at Mrs Poulteney's, and later Charles discovers that Sam's intentions towards Mary are serious; he promises to ask Mrs Tranter if she will permit Sam to court the girl.

NOTES AND GLOSSARY

Ursa . . . **bear:** Charles is punning on Sam's 'Er, sir'; *ursa* is the Latin word for a female bear

primum mobile: (*Latin*) first mover

Chapter 16

The story continues with the author deliberately intruding his own comments and explanations and, in particular, seeing his Victorian novel through twentieth-century eyes. After their quarrel Ernestina is for a while deferential to Charles, but when he goes to sleep whilst she is reading a sentimental poem to him she throws the book at him. Charles tires, however, of constant discussion about furnishing their future, but as yet unfound, house and next afternoon he is 'allowed' to go on another of his geological expeditions. He makes his way to Ware Commons and there he finds, not only an excellent test, but also, predictably, Sarah Woodruff. She is not pleased to see him, and their meeting ends with her telling him that the French Lieutenant will never return because he is married.

NOTES AND GLOSSARY:

de rigeur:	(*French*) required by fashion
Cupid:	see note to Chapter 7
Maid Marian:	Robin Hood's sweetheart
Mrs Caroline Norton:	(1808–77), an Irish poet, author of *The Lady of La Garaye* (1862)
Sheridan:	Richard Brinsley Sheridan (1751–1816), a dramatist, politician and manager of Drury Lane Theatre, London
Melbourne:	Lord Melbourne (1779–1848), English statesman, Prime Minister 1834–41; charged in 1836 with seducing Mrs Norton (see above) but was exonerated of blame
crim. con.:	abbreviation of 'criminal conversation', that is, 'adultery'
Florence Nightingale:	(1820–1910) nurse and hospital reformer during the Crimean War
Lady of the Lamp:	Florence Nightingale
John Stuart Mill:	(1806–73), English philosopher and reformer
Gibson Girl:	Charles Dana Gibson (1867–1944), American artist and illustrator; his 'Gibson Girl' drawings became the vogue at the turn of the century
Lavater's *Physiognomy*:	Johann Kaspar Lavater (1741–1801), Swiss physiognomist and poet; *Physiognomy* was translated into English in 1793
Madame Bovary:	Gustave Flaubert (1821–80), French novelist, published *Madame Bovary* in 1857

Chapter 17

That evening Charles accompanies Ernestina and Mrs Tranter to a concert of religious songs. Whist the visiting soprano is singing, Charles considers his relationship with Tina in the light of what he is beginning to realise is his entanglement with Sarah. He feels that he has perhaps made a mistake in engaging himself to Tina. The author cynically ends this section with Charles's thought that when he is married things will be all right – financially and sexually; love is mentioned only as an afterthought. Whilst Charles thus meditates, Sam's relationship with Mary is also examined, and we realise that Sam's feeling for Mary is much more honest than Charles's feeling for Tina.

NOTES AND GLOSSARY:

Ramadan: ninth month of the Moslem year; the most important religious fast of the faith

vert espérance: (*French*) literally 'hopeful' or 'lively' green; here it suggests the sprightliness of the life-force represented by a bright green

Balmoral boots: a kind of boots which lace up in the front

Handel and Bach: German composers; George Frederick Handel (1685–1759) and Johann Sebastian Bach (1685–1750)

Byron: see note to Chapter 3

moue: (*French*) pout

Leech [*footnote*]: see note to Chapter 5

A demang, madymosselle: this is Sam's version of the French '*A demain, mademoiselle*', that is, 'Until tomorrow, miss'

Chapter 18

After a couple of days spent entirely in the company of Tina and Mrs Tranter, Charles has an unexpected free afternoon because Tina has a migraine. He feels very restless and finally decides to go on an expedition to Ware Commons, but to avoid the area where Sarah walks. Whilst he is searching for tests, Sarah appears, offers him two that she has found and engages him in conversation. Though he had previously always taken the initiative, he now feels that propriety is affronted and tries to escape without further involvement. We are made aware both of his hypocrisy and of his male chauvinism. Sarah, in an intense and desperate mood, begs him to give her an hour of his time so that she can talk to him about what has happened to her. She suggests an assignation, to which he reluctantly agrees. This leaves him feeling as if he had deserted Tina by suddenly going to China, but, in fact, it is an emotional, not a physical desertion that has occurred.

NOTES AND GLOSSARY:

Echinocorys scutata: technical name for a particular kind of fossilised shellfish
déboulis: (*French*) a rough heap of stones
Micraster: a technical term for a particular kind of fossil
status quo: (*Latin*) existing state of things
Odysseus: the hero of Homer's *Odyssey*
Doric: architectural term referring to a strong, simple form of Greek architecture
Calypso: queen of the island Ogygia on which Odysseus was wrecked. She kept him there for seven years by her charms
Darwin: see note to Chapter 2

Chapter 19

That evening Charles entertains Tina, Mrs Tranter and Dr Grogan to dinner in his room at the White Lion. When the evening is over he and Dr Grogan escort the ladies back home and then proceed to Dr Grogan's house where they indulge in whisky and cheroots. The conversation comes round to Sarah Woodruff, whom Grogan diagnoses as suffering from 'obscure melancholia'; he asserts that though she could be cured by confiding in a sympathetic listener, she does not, in fact, wish to be cured. Meanwhile, Sarah herself lies asleep at Mrs Poulteney's together with Millie, the 'upstairs maid'. Fowles now explains that the twentieth-century reader might suspect lesbianism but that Victorian women often slept together and there was nothing sexual between them. The story returns to Charles and Grogan, who are now discussing palaeontology and move on to agree about their reverence for Darwin.

NOTES AND GLOSSARY:

Disraeli: see note to Chapter 3; Disraeli, born a Jew, was baptised into the Christian faith as a boy
comme il faut: (*French*) as it should be, proper
souffrante: (*French*) suffering
Hoffmann's Tales: Ernst Theodor Hoffmann (1776–1822), German writer and caricaturist whose *Tales* are the basis for Offenbach's opera *Tales of Hoffmann*

Dulce est desipere: (*Latin*) this actually means 'It is sweet to act foolishly'; from the Roman poet Horace, *Odes*, XII, 27

Gregorian telescope: reflecting telescope invented by James Gregory (1638–75)

Bentham: Jeremy Bentham (1748–1832), English philosopher and law reformer

Parian: marble from the island of Paros in Greéce

Voltaire: François Marie Arouet de Voltaire (1694–1778), French writer, the embodiment of the French Enlightenment of the eighteenth century

Gladstone: see note to Chapter 3

Vital Religion: Vitalism is a metaphysical doctrine which holds that in every living organism there is an entity not entirely composed of inanimate parts. It essentially refutes atheism and agnosticism and would thus be anathema to Dr Grogan

Chartist: see note to Chapter 3

Augustan: belonging to the period of elegance and refinement of the eighteenth century

Burke: Edmund Burke (1729–97), Anglo-Irish statesman and political writer

Matthew Arnold: (1822–88) English poet, critic and educationist

German doctor: Dr Hartmann; see note below

jarvey: a hackney-coach

Dr Hartmann: Eduard von Hartmann (1842–1906), German metaphysical philosopher who wrote about the human unconscious

George Morland: (1763–1804) English painter of country subjects

Birket Foster: (1825–99) English painter of delicate, poetic landscapes and rustic scenes

Lyell: see note to Chapter 3

Buffon: George Louis Leclerc, Comte de Buffon (1707–88), French naturalist

Darwin: see note to Chapter 2

Archbishop Usher: James Usher (1581–1656), Archbishop of Armagh in Ireland

Gosse: Philip Henry Gosse (1810–88), English naturalist and marine biologist

Crusoe . . . Man Friday: from *Robinson Crusoe* (1719) by Daniel Defoe (?1660–1731)

carbonari: members of a secret political society in early nineteenth-century Naples, aiming to establish a republican government

Chapter 20

Charles meets Sarah as she had requested, and she makes her confession to him: the shipwrecked sailor, Varguennes, seriously wounded, had been taken in by the Talbots and only she could converse with him in French. She fell in love with him, and when he was recovered and about to return to France he begged her to accompany him. After an initial refusal she had followed him to Weymouth, and there she realised that he was completely false. Nevertheless, she asserts that in a mood of self-immolation she had given herself to him.

The stylised romanticism of the setting of this scene with its 'pretty' vocabulary: 'dell . . . dogwood . . . minute green amphitheatre . . . primroses and violets . . . wild strawberry' ties in with the brief reference to Pre-Raphaelite art, but until later in the novel we are unaware of the significance of this connotation.

NOTES AND GLOSSARY:

Miss Anning:	see note to Chapter 8
al fresco:	(*Italian*) in the open air
demi-monde:	(*French*) literally, 'half-world'; it refers to a class of women of low social standing and doubtful morals
Paul and Virginia:	the children's names are taken from *Paul et Virginie* (1788) by the French novelist, Jacques-Henri Bernadin de St Pierre (1737–1814), who was a friend and follower of Rousseau (see note to Chapter 10)
Pre-Raphaelite:	the Pre-Raphaelite Brotherhood was an aesthetic movement of painters and poets, begun round about 1850, aiming to bring back beauty and feeling into art
Millais:	Sir John Everett Millais (1829–96), a member of the Pre-Raphaelite Brotherhood
Ford Madox Brown:	(1821–93) a member of the Pre-Raphaelite Brotherhood
Constable:	John Constable (1776–1837), English landscape painter
Palmer:	Samuel Palmer (1805–81), English landscape painter
abbey of Thélème:	from François Rabelais's (?1494–?1553) *Gargantua*, Chapter 52; Gargantua built the abbey to be the opposite of an ordinary abbey or monastery; its only rule was 'Do what you like'

Chapter 21

Sarah completes her confession, explaining that after he returned to France, Varguennes wrote to her that he was married and she replied that she never wanted to see him again. However, she has told no one except Charles of this sequel, obscurely wishing people to see her in a bad light. Charles is perplexed, but tries to persuade her to leave Lyme. As they talk they hear Sam and Mary coming towards them; they conceal themselves and watch the other couple flirting and kissing. It is an emotive moment for them both, and when Sarah smiles at Charles in complicity he almost loses his head. However, any crisis is averted, and they part, with Sarah leaving first and Charles waiting behind for a while.

NOTES AND GLOSSARY:
in flagrante delicto: (*Latin*) in the very act

Chapter 22

Charles, returning to Lyme, realises that he has been taking risks and decides to end his involvement with Sarah by putting the whole matter in Mrs Tranter's hands. When he arrives back, however, he is positively relieved to find an urgent telegram bidding him to visit his uncle. He believes that his uncle may be about to give him Winsyatt, the family manor, or at least a slightly smaller house in the village, and he conveys this thought to Ernestina, who urges him to try to get Winsyatt itself.

We are shown here that Ernestina is essentially a Philistine, lacking in taste, for her intentions are to get rid of the priceless Carolean and Tudor furniture and the valuable pictures, which she does not recognise as such, and replace them with modern furnishings.

NOTES AND GLOSSARY:
Carolean:	from the time of Kings Charles I and II of England in the seventeenth century
Tudor:	from the time of the Tudor monarchs of England in the late fifteenth and sixteenth centuries
Gobelins:	tapestries from the famous Paris factory of the Gobelins, founded in the fifteenth century
Claude:	Claude Lorraine (1600–82), French landscape painter
Tintoretto:	name given to Jacopo Robusti (1518–94), one of the greatest of the Venetian painters
Crystal Palace:	built for the Great Exhibition of 1851

Chapter 23

This short chapter takes Charles to Winsyatt, which he enters with a proprietorial air. The reader guesses, though he does not, that some shock awaits him. However, we leave him waiting for his uncle whilst we follow Sarah home from Ware Commons; we realise that she deliberately allows herself to be seen by Mrs Fairley, and again we are left wondering.

NOTES AND GLOSSARY:

Baucis: wife of the aged Phrygian, Philemon; the couple were renowned for their hospitable entertainment of Zeus and Hermes

Palladian: in the neo-classical style of the Italian architect Andrea Palladio (1508–80)

the younger Wyatt: Sir Mathew Digby Wyatt (1820–77), an English architect from a family of architects

Chapter 24

Charles is now back in Lyme, and we learn through his conversation with Ernestina that his sixty-seven-year-old uncle is getting married and may therefore have an heir. Ernestina is extremely angry and behaves in a very unladylike fashion, much to Charles's dismay. Hard upon this disaster follows the news that Mrs Poulteney has dismissed Sarah and that the girl has disappeared. Everyone fears suicide, and a search is going on; Charles alone knows where she might be found, but he realises that he is unable to tell anyone.

Chapter 25

For Charles, the third catastrophe is a note from Sarah, begging him to meet her again. Unwisely, he tells Sam to find out who brought the note. A second note arrives, written in French, and by ill-luck Sam learns who has sent it. Charles forbids him to tell anyone and, despite the approaching thunderstorm, he rushes out.

NOTES AND GLOSSARY:

Je vous . . . la ferme: (*French*) I have waited for you all day. I pray you – a woman begs you upon her knees to help her in her despair. I shall pass the night in prayer for your coming. At dawn I shall be at the little barn close by the sea, reached by the first footpath to the left after the farm.

Chapter 26

This chapter opens with indeterminate thoughts of blackmail on Sam's part; it proceeds with a flashback to the meeting at Winsyatt in which Charles is told of his uncle's intended marriage to the widowed Mrs Tomkins. All the assertions that she is not an adventuress convince us that that is exactly what she is – a phenomenon very common in nineteenth-century novels.

In nineteeth-century terms this change in Charles's fortunes puts him at considerable disadvantage with regard to his forthcoming marriage to Ernestina, and we realise that it adds to his doubts about the wisdom of his engagement.

NOTES AND GLOSSARY:

imprimatur: (*Latin*) sanction
ducatur in matrimonium: (*Latin*) command to marriage
faute de mieux: (*French*) for want of something better
Joe Manton: Joseph Manton (1760–1835) was a noted English gunsmith
rentier: person living on dividends from property

Chapter 27

We are now back in Lyme once again. After Charles has rushed out in Chapter 25, he goes to see Dr Grogan, to whom he gives a full but slightly slanted account of his relationship with Sarah. By subtle shifts of emphasis, encouraged by Charles's hints, Grogan puts the whole affair in a different light, making Sarah appear the pursuer and Charles the victim. Grogan decides to go and see Sarah in Charles's stead and he suggests that she will probably have to be placed in a private asylum; Charles has a momentary twinge of guilt at this thought. The chapter ends with Grogan giving Charles an account of a trial to read.

NOTES AND GLOSSARY:

Darwin: see note to Chapter 2
The Origin of Species: see note to Chapter 8
good Samaritan: see note to Chapter 6
in extremis: (*Latin*) at the point of death
de profundis: (*Latin*) out of the depths
de altis: (*Latin*) from the heights
'I am cast . . . revenged': see the Bible, Jonah 2:4: 'I am cast out of thy sight; yet I will look again toward thy holy temple.' Grogan, as usual, alters the quotation to make his point.

Socrates:	(?469–399BC) Greek philosopher
Know thyself:	words inscribed on the temple of Apollo at Delphi in Greece
Malthus:	Thomas Malthus (1766–1834), English economist

Chapter 28

Charles reads what Grogan has given him and finds that it is an account of a trial, together with some psychiatric case histories of hysteria in young women. This has the opposite effect from what Grogan had intended, for Charles begins to question the account he had given the doctor and finally blames himself for the whole affair. At dawn he makes a decision.

NOTES AND GLOSSARY:

Hugo:	Victor Hugo (1802–85), French poet, novelist and playwright
Balzac:	Honoré de Balzac (1799–1850), French novelist
George Sand:	Pseudonym of Amandine Aurore Lucie Dupin (1804–76), French novelist
Dr Karl Matthaei:	(1770–1847), German medical psychologist
Sir Galahad . . . Guinevere:	characters from the stories of King Arthur and the knights of the Round Table
Pontius Pilate:	the Roman Governor who washed his hands of responsibility for the death of Jesus; see the Bible, Matthew 27:24

Chapter 29

Charles decides to set out and find Sarah. He starts off early on the path to the Undercliff. The setting for his walk is presented in idyllic terms. Fowles deliberately romanticises the natural beauties in the first part of this chapter; in contrast, however, Charles himself feels that everything is hostile towards him. The contrast is accentuated in the second part of the chapter when he reaches the stone hut where he expects to see Sarah. The vocabulary now becomes threatening, the jungle tiger replacing the earlier fox and roe-deer, until the last paragraph seems like the introduction to a Gothic horror story as Charles enters the derelict building and sees Sarah's black bonnet hanging from a nail.

NOTES AND GLOSSARY:

Pisanello:	Vittore Pisanello (?1395–?1455), Italian painter, famous for his paintings of animals

Chapter 30

Chronologically, this chapter follows Sarah's arrival back home at the end of Chapter 23. By this time, Mrs Fairley has done her evil worst and has blackened Sarah to Mrs Poulteney, who calls the girl to her and dismisses her. For the first time Sarah responds with the full force of her bitterness, touching Mrs Poulteney where she is most vulnerable, with the hint that God may not listen to her in the world to come. At this, Mrs Poulteney falls in a faint and Sarah goes from the room, leaving Mrs Fairley to minister to her mistress.

NOTES AND GLOSSARY:

Parthian shaft: a shot saved for the moment of departure (the ancient Parthian horsemen shot backward as they retreated)

Jezebel: evil woman (from the biblical account in I Kings 16 of Ahab's marriage to the heathen Jezebel and of his turning to worship idols)

Chapter 31

We return to Charles. In the stone hut he finds Sarah sleeping peacefully. At first he wants to rush away, but as he reaches the door he finds himself calling her name involuntarily. Sarah awakes, and explanations between them ensue. Suddenly Sarah tells him the truth – she had deliberately allowed Mrs Fairley to see her. It is clear to Charles that she is passionately in love with him and for a brief moment he resists; then they fall into each other's arms. As the realisation of what is happening comes to him he pushes her away and rushes out of the door.

NOTES AND GLOSSARY:

Matthaei: see note to Chapter 28

Hegel: Georg Wilhelm Friedrich Hegel (1770–1831), German philosopher

Catullus: Caius Valerius Catullus (?84–?54BC), Latin poet who wrote passionate love lyrics

Sappho: (born ?650BC) Greek poetess of love

Chapter 32

Meanwhile, Ernestina has a restless night after her disagreement with Charles and she confides to her diary her intention of bending herself to his will. The use of a diary to impart information to the reader is a typical device of the Victorian novelist. Downstairs the next morning Sam, who had been left orders by Charles to pack ready to leave Lyme, has imparted this information to Mary. The girl's distress is slightly relieved by Mrs Tranter giving her a few hours off to be with Sam.

NOTES AND GLOSSARY:

Janus-like: hypocritical; Janus was the Roman god of gates and had two heads, looking in opposite directions

peignoir: see note to Chapter 5

Chapter 33

When Charles rushes from the stone hut at the end of Chapter 31 he is dismayed to see Sam and Mary approaching him and, of course, the circumstances look more suspicious than they are. He accosts Sam and tries to explain the situation away, offering the young man money which Sam refuses, both of them recognising it as a bribe. Charles then returns to the hut, gives Sarah some money and persuades her to go to Exeter without returning to Lyme.

Chapter 34

When Charles returns to Lyme he changes his clothes and goes to see Ernestina. Though he does not know it, the news that he is intending to leave Lyme and go to London has already reached her, and she is not pleased. He explains that he must tell her father of his changed circumstances and promises to deliver a letter from Ernestina herself. With a rather formal embrace he attempts to leave her, but she detains him and he is forced to kiss her lips, though he feels this as a kind of pollution after the incident with Sarah earlier that day. On his way out at last, he buys Mary's silence with half a sovereign.

NOTES AND GLOSSARY:

Aphrodite: the Greek name for Venus, goddess of love

Mrs Bloomer: Amelia Bloomer (1818–94), American champion of women's rights; she introduced the full long 'bloomers' as a female form of trousers

Chapter 35

This chapter is a digression in which the author castigates Victorian society, criticising its flagrant insincerity which overtly lauded morality and secretly practised, permitted and encouraged immorality. Without mentioning Charles, Fowles makes clear his view of the hypocrisy which governed Charles's words and actions; he also uses this diatribe to expatiate on the liaison between Thomas Hardy and Tryphena Sparks and finally to reflect on why Sam and Mary are making their way to the stone hut (Chapter 33); he draws a comparison between Mary and Tryphena Sparks. It is worth realising that this novel was written in 1967 just after the information about Hardy and his cousin Tryphena had been made public, and that it covers the very period during which, it is alleged, Hardy and Tryphena were engaged.

NOTES AND GLOSSARY:

Marquis de Sade: Donatien Alphonse François, Marquis de Sade (1740–1814), French writer who wrote about and indulged in vicious sexual practices; the word 'sadism' is derived from his name

Dr Bowdler: Thomas Bowdler (1754–1825), responsible for 'bowdlerising' the works of Shakespeare by omitting everything which 'cannot with propriety be read aloud in a family'

Malthus: see note to Chapter 27

Dickens: see note to Chapter 7

Mayhew: Henry Mayhew (1812–87) wrote a social survey, *London Labour and the London Poor* (1851–62)

Thomas Hardy: (1840–1928) English novelist whose novels were placed in Dorset and the surrounding counties

Pandora's box: mythical box which held all the evils of the world; they were released when the box was opened rashly

Edmund Gosse: (1845–1928) English poet and critic, son of Philip Gosse (see note to Chapter 19)

Atreids . . . Mycenae: statues uncovered in excavations at Mycenae; they represent members of the infamous house of Atreus, whose tragic fates are related in Aeschylus's (525–456BC) *Oresteia* trilogy

Tryphena: the story of Tryphena and Hardy was first published in *Providence and Mr Hardy* (1966) by Lois Deacon and Terry Coleman

Chapter 36

We are now transported to Exeter and to Endicott's Family Hotel where Sarah has taken up residence. It is a rather sordid little hotel, ill-furnished and ill-equipped, but Sarah has taken two rooms there and, after an initial period of parsimony, has spent a little money to make herself comfortable. Her purchases include a nightgown, an elegant shawl and a roll of bandage. We leave her at the end of the chapter drinking a cup of tea and eating a meat pie.

As often in this novel the details of events are more significant than they appear; we only become aware of the significance of Sarah's purchases several chapters further on.

NOTES AND GLOSSARY:

Charles Wesley: (1707–88) English hymn-writer and evangelical preacher

Ralph Leigh: George and Ralph Leigh owned a pottery-manufacturing firm in Cobridge, in the Potteries, round about 1839. They specialised in making Toby jugs

Chapter 37

After leaving Ernestina (Chapter 34), Charles goes to London to see her father and explain the change in his fortune brought about by his uncle's impending marriage. Mr Freeman, who is extremely wealthy, accepts Charles's word that he had no inkling of this when he proposed to Ernestina. After reading his daughter's letter he agrees that the marriage must proceed. He then proposes that at some time in the future Charles should become a partner in his business. The idea of 'trade' is, in true Victorian fashion, repugnant to Charles's view of how a gentleman should live, but he cannot bring himself to say so. Ironically, Mr Freeman introduces the idea of evolution to imply that the impoverished aristocracy must adapt themselves to changes in their environment.

NOTES AND GLOSSARY:

Mr Jorrocks: a character in the sporting novels of R. S. Surtees (1803–64); Jorrocks was a grocer

Marcus Aurelius: (AD121–180) Roman Emperor

Lord Palmerston: (1784–1865) Anglo-Irish statesman, Prime Minister in 1855–8 and 1859–65

Jesus . . . Satan: see the Bible, Matthew 4:1–11, Mark 1:12–13 and Luke 4:1–13

pilgrim . . . Progress: a reference to *Pilgrim's Progress* by John Bunyan (1628–88)

savoir-vivre: (*French*) good breeding, knowledge of proper behaviour

Corinthian: architectural term to describe a very ornate form of architecture

Chapter 38

By the time that Charles leaves the Freeman mansion it is dark. He walks about aimlessly, observing the lower classes around him and beginning to feel that they have advantages that he lacks: they are, he believes, happy and free, and he is neither. By chance, his wanderings lead him into Oxford Street where he comes upon Mr Freeman's great store, and he realises that he can never be involved in trade. The author then undermines any feelings of superiority the reader may be indulging in by comparing Charles's attitudes with those that we ourselves may well display – though based not on aristocratic, but on social mores. Charles feels trapped and is suddenly furious with Mr Freeman. He takes a cab, looking forward to milk punch and champagne at the end of his journey.

NOTES AND GLOSSARY:

great Reform Bill: see Fowles's comments in Chapter 16 and those in the Introduction above

Candide: title character of a novel (1759) by Voltaire (see note to Chapter 19)

nouveau riche: (*French*) newly rich; the term refers to the class of people in the nineteenth century who made money from trade, rather than inherited it

preux chevaliers: (*French*) brave knights

New Testament . . . Wilderness: see note to Chapter 37

Chapter 39

Charles goes to his club where he immediately meets two old university friends, both of them dissolute and corrupt. They ply him with alcohol until he is drunk and then take him to a vulgar striptease club where, watching the performance for a while, he is torn between disgust and lust. He leaves and takes another cab, passing through streets lined with prostitutes. As they go along a more deserted street he sees a girl who reminds him of Sarah, and he goes home with her for the night.

NOTES AND GLOSSARY:

Mytton: John Mytton (1796–1834), English sportsman and eccentric who specialised in foolhardy physical feats and who gambled away a vast fortune

Casanova: Giovanni Jacopo Casanova de Seingalt (1725–98), Italian adventurer, famous for his sexual escapades

muses' shrine . . . *Metonymia* . . . *Puella*: a complicated joke;

metonymia is the Greek word for our own
'metonymy', the substitution of one word ('girl',
Latin *puella*) for another related to it (Venus, a
goddess to be worshipped at a shrine)

Terpsichore: muse of dancing

***Carmina Priapea XLIV*:** from a collection of eighty erotic poems in
Poetae Latini Minores, edited by Jacob Bährens
(1879)

Camargo petticoats: Marie Camargo (1710–70), French ballet star; she
introduced calf-length ballet skirts and became a
fashion-setter

Roederer's champagne: one of the famous brands of champagne

Heliogabalus: Roman Emperor (AD218–222)

Agamemnon: commander of the Greek army which beseiged
Troy to try to recover Helen

***The History of the Human Heart*:** anonymous erotic novel, subtitled *The
Adventures of a Young Gentleman*

Cleland . . . *Fanny Hill*: John Cleland (1709–89) published *Fanny Hill*
in 1750

***danseuse*:** (*French*) dancer

Chapter 40

The girl's room is shabby but clean, and Charles learns that in an
adjoining room is her little daughter. The girl offers him food, but he
accepts only some wine. His lust begins to diminish, and he is over-
taken by a feeling of nausea. When the prostitute strips naked,
Charles's desire briefly flares up; he begins to undress and goes
towards the bed. At this point he asks the girl her name and when she
replies 'Sarah', he is unable to contain his nausea any longer and
vomits repeatedly into her pillow.

This incident is meant to suggest disgust and revulsion, and the final
scene acts as a sign to Charles of what may eventually become of Sarah
Woodruff. For the reader it is a typical Victorian novelistic
coincidence that the girl who looks a little like Sarah should turn out to
bear Sarah's name.

NOTES AND GLOSSARY:

***peignoir*:** see note to Chapter 5

Etty: William Etty (1787–1849), English figure painter,
famous for his nudes

Pygmalion: Pygmalion was a legendary king of Cyprus who fell
in love with a statue which was given life by
Aphrodite

Chapter 41

Sam, not knowing when Charles intends to return, waits up for him
and is not very pleased when his master comes back late, angry and still
somwhat drunk. This chapter opens the next morning with Sam complaining about Charles to the housekeeper and hinting at even worse
revelations. When Charles rings the bell to summon Sam we are taken
back to the previous night and the moment when Charles is sick over
the bed. The prostitute tends him for a while and then goes to call a
cab. Whilst she is gone the child awakes and cries, and Charles goes
through to comfort her. Oddly, it gives him a kind of comfort to be
moved to pity and sympathy; thus, when he leaves he places five
sovereigns on the table.

NOTES AND GLOSSARY:

Charles's . . . Sartrean experience: that is, he was experiencing
comfort from the realities around him; Jean-Paul
Sartre (1905–80) was the principal proponent of
existentialism

Chapter 42

When Charles awakes next morning, Sam brings him tea and two
letters, one from Dr Grogan in reply to a letter from Charles conceal-
ing what had happened on his last morning at Lyme; Grogan warns
him that Sarah may pursue him to London. The second letter contains
only an address, and we learn later that Sam has steamed this one open
and is aware of its contents.

Charles now tells Sam that they are to return to Lyme next day, and
Sam confesses his intention to propose to Mary and hints that he would
like some money to set himself up in a draper's shop. Charles refuses at
first, but afterwards half succumbs to what the reader recognises as
Sam's attempt at blackmail.

NOTES AND GLOSSARY:

éclaircissement: (*French*) clarification
sub tegmine fagi: (*Latin*) under the shade of a beech-tree; from
    Virgil, *Eclogues*, I, 1
à la lettre: (*French*) by letter
Absolvitur: (*Latin*) absolution
ante: (*Latin*) before
Stanislavski: professional name of Konstantin Sergeivitch
    Alexeyev (1865–1938), a Russian actor and pro-
    ducer who put forward the theory that an actor had

	to create reality by actually being the part he played
Uriah Heep:	hypocritical character in Dickens's *David Copperfield*, who always pretended humility as a foil to his cunning

Chapter 43

On the train journey to Exeter Charles considers his position and recalls the address in the second letter – 'Endicott's Family Hotel'. He regrets that Sarah's note showed no sign of guilt, nor did she ask anything of him; however, he now decides that he will put the past behind him and marry Ernestina. When Sam asks if they are to stay the night in Exeter, Charles replies in the negative. They take a carriage to Lyme, and the chapter ends with Charles falling asleep.

Here we see the beginning of the traditional moral ending of a Victorian novel in which the hero reforms, puts the evils of his past life behind him and vows to be faithful to his first and true love.

Chapter 44

When they arrive in Lyme, Charles quickly goes to Mrs Tranter's, where a touchingly romantic scene ensues between him and Ernestina in which he gives her the present of a brooch. He then confesses his involvement with Sarah, and she forgives him. The novel ends, again conventionally for a Victorian novel, with a brief explanation of what happens to the other characters and draws a moral by consigning Mrs Poulteney to hell.

But this is not the end of the novel; there are still eighteen chapters to go. There is a disjuncture in the two novel threads – nineteenth and twentieth century – which Fowles has been presenting simultaneously. What we are shown here is the first possible ending; the way a Victorian romance would end; it is not a typical ending of a twentieth-century novel.

Chapter 45

Now the author confesses that the two previous chapters represented what might have been, rather than what was. The hypothesis is dismissed and we are taken back to the moment of decision broached in Chapter 43, that is, Sam's question as to whether they are to stay the night in Exeter. This time Charles decides to stay at the Ship Inn for the night. He tells Sam to take the baggage to the inn whilst he stretches his legs. As soon as Sam has gone with the cab to the inn Charles makes for

Endicott's Family Hotel. He is unaware that Sam who, as we know, had read Sarah's note, has swiftly prepared their rooms at the Ship and reached Endicott's before him, taking up a position from which he can watch his master. Charles arrives and disappears inside the hotel. Sam watches for a little longer and then walks away.

NOTES AND GLOSSARY:

Delphic: ambiguous or enigmatic; from the Greek oracle at Delphi

browns: copper coins

Chapter 46

Inside the hotel, Charles asks for Sarah, and the proprietress tells him that she has sprained her ankle and is confined to her room. Charles had hoped to talk to Sarah in a downstairs sitting-room, but is persuaded to go up to her own room. There he finds Sarah, dressed in her nightgown, with her shawl round her shoulders and her feet on a stool. After a few moments' small talk they find themselves drawn to each other. They embrace wildly, passionately and move into the bedroom; intercourse follows immediately.

If we cast our minds back to the purchases Sarah made earlier we shall realise that she had carefully planned this seduction scene.

Chapter 47

After the first ecstasy, Charles feels bitter guilt, as though Ernestina and her father were both condemning him, and guilt that he has behaved badly towards Sarah. He now declares that he will break his engagement and marry Sarah. She insists that he cannot, though she loves him. When he goes back into the sitting-room to dress he sees blood on his shirt-tail, and the realisation that she was a virgin comes upon him. Strangely, he now treats her as if not having had intercourse with Varguennes were more of a sin than had she done so. Then he suddenly realises that she is walking normally, with no sign of a sprained ankle, and, like the reader, he realises that he has been lured into a trap. However, having finally entangled him, Sarah now rejects him; she begs him to leave, and suddenly Charles, without a word, leaves the room.

Chapter 48

Charles quickly leaves Endicott's Hotel and plunges aimlessly into an unsavoury area of Exeter. He sees a church and suddenly feels the need to go in and pray. At the door he meets a young curate who is locking up; the curate asks Charles to lock up after he has finished his prayers and bring the key to the curate's house. Inside the church, Charles is racked with anguish, knowing that he is wronging both Sarah and Ernestina. An agnostic, he finds himself in an agony of religious doubt which appears to be finally resolved by his decision that he must be true to his vision of Sarah.

The moralising of this chapter belongs to the Victorian novel, but its agonies are existential and its conclusions are of the twentieth century; a Victorian hero would have rejected Sarah and believed that morality tied him to Ernestina.

NOTES AND GLOSSARY:

scumbered: (*obsolete*) dung-covered
Mater Dolorosa: (*Latin*) grieving mother; referring to the Virgin Mary
Grünewald: Matthias Grünewald (?1480–1528), a German painter
Bradlaugh: Charles Bradlaugh (1833–91), a social reformer and militant atheist
Lyell: see note to Chapter 3
Darwin: see note to Chapter 2
render unto Caesar: from the Bible, Matthew 22:21, 'Render therefore unto Caesar the things which are Caesar's; and unto God the things that are God's'; see also Mark 12:17 and Luke 20:25
In Memoriam: (1850) a long poem by Tennyson written in memory of his friend Arthur Hallam, who died in 1833; see also note to Chapter 6
St Paul . . . Damascus: St Paul was converted as he journeyed on the road to Damascus; see the Bible, Acts 9:1–8
Uffizi: the famous art gallery in Florence, dating from about the end of the sixteenth century

Chapter 49

Charles returns the key to the curate and decides that he must do the honourable thing – break formally with Ernestina before he embraces Sarah again. He walks through the rain towards the Ship where Sam meets him. After a bath and a good supper he writes to Sarah, telling her that he wishes to marry her; yet the Victorian Charles keeps the letter until the morning with the arrogant thought that Sarah should suffer without him one more night. Next morning Sam is sent with the letter to Endicott's Family Hotel; the letter contains a brooch, the very brooch that Charles gave Ernestina in his imagination in Chapter 44. Sam returns and says that there is no answer to the letter, which persuades Charles to believe that Sarah has received and kept the brooch.

We learn later that Sam has not taken the letter to the hotel and that he has appropriated the brooch, which he later gives to Mary. The chapter ends with Sam telling Mary what he knows – which we realise is practically everything – and we become aware that he is about to desert Charles.

NOTES AND GLOSSARY:

en passage:	(*French*) passing through
Tractarian schism:	break from orthodoxy by an English High Church movement based on a series of 'Tracts for the Times' (1833–41)
Tennyson:	see note to Chapter 6
Clough:	Arthur Hugh Clough (1819–61), English poet
Arnold:	see note to Chapter 19
Hardy:	see note to Chapter 35
Mill:	see note to Chapter 16
Gladstone:	see note to Chapter 3
Charles Kingsley:	(1819–75), English poet and novelist
Darwin:	see note to Chapter 2
Pre-Raphaelites:	see note to Chapter 20
Dr Jekyll and Mr Hyde:	a story by Robert Louis Stevenson (1850–94), published in 1886

Chapter 50

Charles proceeds to Lyme and immediately goes to Mrs Tranter's house. He tells Ernestina that he is breaking the engagement and, though he tries to do it gently, Ernestina is distraught. He now realises that, despite her follies, she loves him; because of this he feels he should tell her about Sarah, but instead he tells her a lie about an old love. Now Ernestina is incensed and threatens him with legal action. He is about to leave when she calls his name and appears to faint; he recognises this for a sham, summons the terrified Mary and goes from the room intending to fetch Dr Grogan and to write to Ernestina's father.

NOTES AND GLOSSARY:

Helen of Troy:	said to have been the most beautiful woman who ever lived
Cleopatra:	Queen of Egypt who had many lovers

Chapter 51

Charles goes to Dr Grogan's house, tells him he has broken off his engagement and asks the doctor to attend to Ernestina. He then goes to his rooms at the White Lion where Sam, who has already heard of the broken engagement, gives him notice. Charles now decides to write to Ernestina's father and then return to Sarah at Exeter that evening. Whilst he is writing, Dr Grogan is announced.

NOTES AND GLOSSARY:
a Judas: the betrayer of Christ
an Ephialtes: a radical Athenian statesman, killed $c.457$BC

Chapter 52

We return to Mrs Tranter's house where Dr Grogan has given Ernestina a sleeping draught. When Mrs Tranter arrives home she finds everything in turmoil. Dr Grogan tells her what has happened and then declares he is off to see Charles. Mary tells Mrs Tranter about her love for Sam and reveals that Sam has left Charles. She is promised that a job will be found for him.

NOTES AND GLOSSARY:
non-sequitur: (*Latin*) something which does not follow logically

Chapter 53

When Grogan leaves Mrs Tranter's house he goes immediately to see Charles, and though their interview begins in acrimony they finally make a sort of peace; Grogan, however, tells Charles to leave Lyme immediately.

NOTES AND GLOSSARY:
Dante: Dante Alighieri (1265–1321), supreme Italian poet whose long poem, the *Divine Comedy*, describes the punishments devised for sinners in the Inferno (Hell)
Antinomians: a sect which held that the moral law is not binding on Christians, since faith alone is sufficient for salvation
Jacta alea est: (*Latin*) 'the die has been cast', the words of Caesar when he was about to cross the Rubicon
Rubicon: the river which bounded Caesar's province; his

crossing of it in 49BC marked the start of the war with Pompey. It means that Charles had passed the point of no return

Chapter 54

Charles now leaves Lyme and makes for Exeter where he goes to Endicott's Family Hotel; there he is told that Sarah left that morning for London. He also learns that Sam did not deliver his letter and the brooch to Sarah that morning. Charles now realises what the reader has known for some time – that Sam is not the ideal gentleman's gentleman but has been constantly deceiving and betraying him.

Chapter 55

Next morning, Charles takes the train to London. He is joined in his carriage by a bearded man wearing a top hat. Charles, his mind on Sarah, vaguely dislikes the stranger. As soon as Charles drops off to sleep, however, the narrator confesses that he himself is the stranger and that Charles is a problem to him, since he is a character in a Victorian novel which cannot have an inconclusive ending, and yet the narrator believes in a freedom for his characters which does not tie them down.

The discussion of narrative technique here presents the reader clearly with the problems the novelist faces. The author tells us that he will offer us two versions of the ending, yet he knows that the one offered last will be seen by the readers as the 'real' ending. Thus, in order not to show prejudice, he tosses a coin to decide in which order the versions shall appear. To some extent, however, because of his doubts, he has predisposed us to accept his second version, though as yet we do not know what the two endings are to be.

NOTES AND GLOSSARY:
Spurgeon: Charles Haddon Spurgeon (1834–92), an English Baptist preacher
nouveau roman: see note on Alain Robbe-Grillet, Chapter 13

Chapter 56

Charles begins to search for Sarah, hiring four detectives to help him, but he finds no trace of her. Then a letter arrives from Mr Freeman's solicitors, asking him to attend at their chambers. Charles goes, attended by his own solicitor, Mr Montague. The result of this summons is that the case of breach of promise against Charles will not go to trial, but Charles is asked to sign an insulting and degrading document which, on Montague's advice, he does. Montague now suggests that Charles should go abroad, and about a week later he decides to do so.

NOTES AND GLOSSARY:

sine die: (*Latin*) with no appointed date
Verrey's: old-established London restaurant for over 275 years, which finally closed down in 1985
prima facie: (*Latin*) at first sight

Chapter 57

We now jump forward twenty months to February 1869. Mary, now married to Sam, has an infant girl and is six months pregnant with the next child. As she walks along Chelsea Embankment one day she happens to see Sarah Woodruff alight from a cab and enter one of the houses.

Sam has done well for himself and is working for Mr Freeman for a good weekly wage. When Mary tells him about Sarah we realise that he has been experiencing some guilt about Charles and is perhaps about to try to expiate it.

NOTES AND GLOSSARY:

Gladstone: see note to Chapter 3
No. 10 Downing Street: the official residence of the British Prime Minister
Mill: see note to Chapter 16
Subjection of Women: published 1869
Girton College: first college for women at Cambridge University, founded in 1869
Catullus: see note to Chapter 31
Faust: legendary figure who sold his soul to the Devil in exchange for a limited life of absolute pleasure

Chapter 58

Meanwhile, Charles has been constantly travelling. After fifteen months abroad he returns to London to see Montague and then goes to America.

NOTES AND GLOSSARY:

alberghi: (*Italian*) inns
Tennyson: see note to Chapter 6

Matthew Arnold [*footnote*]: see note to Chapter 19

Pocahontas: (1595–1617) a beautiful Red Indian girl who saved
an English colonist from death at her father's
hands

pour la dot comme . . . *figure*: (*French*) as much for the dowry as for the
looks

Chapter 59

Charles has a bad voyage to America; when he arrives in Boston,
however, he finds that he likes the country and its people. He is
popular with the young American women, but constantly has Sarah in
his mind. His restless travels are briefly recounted until, at the end of
the chapter, we learn that through the offices of Sam, now the father of
a son as well as a daughter, Sarah has been found. Charles books the
next ship to Europe.

NOTES AND GLOSSARY:

Nathaniel Lodge: The Lodges were a famous Boston family, but
Fowles invented Nathaniel to fit in with his time
scale; the American edition changes the name to
'the elder Dana'; Richard Henry Dana (1787–
1879) was an American poet and journalist

Lowell circle: an influential family in the United States,
descended from early settlers

the master: Henry James (1843–1916), American novelist who
left America and settled in Rye, England

Andrew Johnson: (1808–75) Seventeenth President of the United
States

Ulysses S. Grant: (1822–85) Eighteenth President of the United
States

Chapter 60

Montague has received only Sarah's address – as we know, though he
does not, from Sam – but he has learned that she goes under the name
of Mrs Roughwood. Charles goes to the address, finds her there and is
astonished to realise that she is living with a group of Pre-Raphaelite
artists, including Rossetti. During their conversation Sarah tells him
that she is no man's mistress but that she does not wish to marry since
she is happy acting as artist's assistant and doing what she wants to do.

Charles presses her to accept him, and she then tells him that she has
known for some time that he had broken his engagement and that she

changed her name and her lodgings after she had seen one of his advertisements seeking news of her. He becomes bitter and accuses her of enjoying destroying his life; as he turns to go she detains him and asks him to see a lady who understands her better than anyone in the world. Reluctantly, he agrees, and after a few minutes a little girl is brought into the room and left there. He inspects the child with intensity and realises that she is his daughter. When Sarah returns, the chapter ends with a very Victorian reconciliation between her and Charles, and the reader is left to believe that they marry and live happily ever after.

This is, however, the penultimate chapter; it is the first version of the ending, the one the narrator knows we shall dismiss when we have read the second version in the last chapter.

NOTES AND GLOSSARY:

Disraeli: see note to Chapter 3

New Woman: term used in latter part of nineteenth century for a woman who sought independence and rejected convention

name of another person: the person was Algernon Charles Swinburne (1837–1909), English poet

John Morley: (1838–1923) English journalist, critic and politician

ménage . . . cinq: (*French*) household of four – or five; the term is usually used derogatively

Mr Ruskin: John Ruskin (1819–1900), English author and critic

Noel Humphreys: Henry Noel Humphreys (1810–79), English artist known particularly for his book designs and illustrations

Christina Rossetti: (1830–94) English poet, sister of Dante Gabriel Rossetti; see note below

Pre-Raphaelite Brotherhood: see note to Chapter 20

Chopin: Frédéric Chopin (1810–49), Polish composer and pianist

Mr Rossetti: Dante Gabriel Rossetti (1828–82), English poet and painter, one of the founders of the Pre-Raphaelite Brotherhood

Chapter 61

This final chapter begins with the stranger in the train, the persona of the narrator, now somewhat changed physically, but still a Victorian narrator, putting back his watch to a time which is about two thirds of the way through the previous chapter; Charles again accuses Sarah of twisting the dagger she has plunged in his breast. As before he turns to go and, as before, she attempts to detain him. Now, however, he speaks harshly to her and goes from the room. As he leaves the house he sees a girl with a small child in her arms, but he does not stop as he takes himself out of Sarah's life for ever.

This is the twentieth-century version of the ending, through which the reader is shown that romantic notions are not fulfilled. If the first version is like the ending of a Victorian novel, this is a little like the ending of D. H. Lawrence's *Sons and Lovers* in which the protagonist, Paul, having parted from his one-time love for ever, walks out of the story.

NOTES AND GLOSSARY:

flânerie:	(*French*) stroll
Breguet:	Abraham-Louis Breguet (1747–1823), a famous Swiss clockmaker
soupirant:	(*French*) suitor
Marx:	see note to Chapter 3
unplumb'd, salt, estranging sea:	from Matthew Arnold's 'To Marguerite', which is quoted in full in Chapter 58

Part 3
Commentary

General comment

The French Lieutenant's Woman is set in the mid-Victorian era, and the story belongs to that period; it is seen simultaneously, however, through the perspectives and sensibilities of both the nineteenth and the twentieth centuries. Thus, some of the characters, while responding to the morals of their own time, display beneath the veneer of Victorian prudery and priggishness a more universal awareness which allows them to see through the limitations of their own lives and to glimpse hopes beyond the restrictions the age lays upon them. This duality has become possible only through the twentieth-century approach to technique in the novel, which maintains that plot is subservient to character and that in order to understand events the reader needs to understand how the characters themselves view those events.

The novel begins, in true nineteenth-century fashion, with meticulous attention to detail: the place, the time, even the weather are established in the first paragraph, and the curiosity of the reader is aroused by the two people walking along the Cobb. By the third paragraph not only has a typical nineteenth-century intrusive narrator found his way into the story, but it has become apparent that it is not an historical novel; Henry Moore is placed beside Michelangelo, and gradually the 'then' and 'now' of Lyme, Ware Cleeves and the southern coastline are compared and paralleled.

If the 'I' of the third paragraph may be thought of as John Fowles, the 'local spy' two paragraphs further on is one of the roles assumed by the narrator who, as we shall see, should not be confused with the author himself. It is apparent, too, that this particular narrator is not omniscient as he observes through his telescope the three characters so far introduced – the two walking along the Cobb, fashionable, conventional, knowable, and the third, a figure from myth, mysterious, standing motionless at the very end of the Cobb, staring with intense concentration out to sea.

The plot of the novel has all the ingredients of a Victorian romance. The engaged couple, Charles and Ernestina (her name is itself an example of Victorian male chauvinism; the daughter, disappointing expectations of the longed-for male heir, is subsumed into masculinity by being given a feminine form of the non-existent brother's name), are attracted to each other, not by love but by a form of propriety. Through their marriage the Freemans will gain a foothold in the aristocracy, while the fortunes of the Smithsons will be given a financial boost. The problems, however, are apparent: Charles, a gentleman by birth, will be marrying into trade; Ernestina, on the other hand, finds that Charles, the dilettante scholar, is unwilling to dedicate his every moment to serving her. Yet the marriage appears to be an appropriate one and, if jealousy is a sign of love, Ernestina clearly has some feelings for Charles, whilst he, for his part, lusts for the moment when, the marriage having taken place, it can be consummated.

Sarah Woodruff is the poor, innocent, harshly treated woman from the lower classes, who discovers a mutual attraction between herself and the handsome hero, Charles. There is a duo of Victorian villains, Mrs Poulteney and Mrs Fairley, a rich uncle trapped into marriage by a scheming widow, Mrs Arabella Tomkins, a kindly aunt and a chorus of lower-class characters – mainly the servants – to comment on events.

At first the story proceeds conventionally. Charles is the pursuer and Sarah the pursued. At the moment when Charles's fortunes are at their lowest ebb, when it appears that he is likely to be disinherited by his uncle, when Mr Freeman is offering him the indignity of a job in trade, when Ernestina is reproaching him in a vulgar and unladylike fashion, the position is subtly reversed; Sarah not so much pursues as entraps Charles, seems to lust after him as no Victorian lady could lust with any propriety and, having found fulfilment through him, promptly deserts him.

The Victorian narrator was quite right to attempt to end the story in Chapter 44. At this point the traditional ending of the nineteenth-century moral novel is presented: the erring lover repents of his wrong-doings and returns to his true love carrying gifts, in Charles's case the dark red morocco box holding the mosaic brooch. He makes his confession, she forgives him, and they live happily ever after – or might have seemed to do so had the narrator not told us to the contrary in an un-Victorian comment that may well help to confirm our beliefs about the falsity of the endings of many Victorian novels.

As we know, however, the story does not end with Chapter 44. The narrator disowns the ending, blaming it on the Hardyesque 'personification of a certain massive indifference to things'; he proceeds to dislocate time so that the plot can return to the point in Chapter 43 which initiates the events leading to the premature ending with Sam's question, 'Are we stayin' the night, sir?' This time, Sam receives a different answer, and the novel is on course for a different ending. Now, interlayered with the nineteenth-century story, a twentieth-century story asserts itself. The seduction of Sarah – or is it of Charles? – is accomplished in a few pages, and the sexual act is not passed over but (unheard of in Victorian fiction) is described in detail.

The disappearance of Sarah and the long search for her take us back again to Victorian times, and the narrator provides us with yet another Victorian ending in the penultimate chapter. There, Charles finds Sarah again and discovers that he has fathered her child; romance takes over and we must assume that the two get married and live happily ever after, though, as we have observed in Chapter 44, the narrator himself had already thrown doubt on the genuineness of 'happy endings'. The final chapter, however, re-introduces the Victorian narrator who, after putting his watch back a quarter of an hour in order to wipe out the previous ending, takes a landau and is driven out of the story. The other 'I' – Fowles? – remains to dislocate time once more. Again we hear Charles's words, 'No. It is as I say. You have not only planted the dagger in my breast, you have delighted in twisting it.' This time, however, no reconciliation takes place. Charles does not learn of his child and he leaves Sarah in anger, never to see her again.

Despite the various attempts at endings, there is, of course, only one plot. Duality appears not in the telling but in the interpreting of events. The reader sees the characters act and react as Victorians, yet, only partially obscured by nineteenth-century propriety, there are rebellious thoughts and unbridled passions. The form of the narration encourages the reader to impose twentieth-century interpretations on the story, and as this happens, the characters themselves move forward into our own time.

Through this dual approach we are constantly aware of the present impinging upon the past. What might in Victorian times have been a straightforward romantic plot has become a psychological thriller, leaving us dissatisfied with all the proffered endings, the first two because they do not ring true and the third because our hearts cry out against it.

Narrative technique

How does one tell a story? The possibilities are numerous, and in this century we have seen, perhaps, more interest in the technique of 'telling' than in the stories themselves. To some extent we may see *The French Lieutenant's Woman* as an attempt to examine narrative technique and to involve the reader in a story which, like life, has not been predetermined and which, amoeba-like, changes shape before our very eyes.

The first chapter, then, has introduced two different narrators; the first is an intrusive nineteenth-century character who indulges in dialogue with his readers; the second is an observer, a man with a telescope*, who looks objectively at the scene and characters before him. Perhaps the presence of even a third narrator can be discerned in the last paragraph of this chapter – this time an omniscient one, viewing both the scene and the characters before him and also the objective narrator and foretelling that his objectivity will be inadequate when he comes to present the enigmatic figure of Sarah. From the outset, then, the identity of the storyteller is ambiguous – a gossipy raconteur? an observer? a god-figure? – and the ambiguity continues throughout the novel. As the story proceeds all three have a hand in it: in the true spirit of the Victorian novel the reader is drawn into discussion of the characters, is accused, in the fashion of Anthony Trollope (1815–82), of particular reactions:

. . . you may despise Charles for his overburden of apparatus, you perhaps despise him for his lack of specialization . . .

(Chapter 8)

and is persuaded out of his prejudices with 'But you must remember . . .' A second narrator observes and describes, whilst a third, erudite and unpredictable, hovers over (or outside) the plot, insisting simultaneously that its telling is 'all imagination' (Chapter 13), that he is playing 'the god-game'†, and that

to be free myself, I must give [Charles], and Tina, and Sarah, even the abominable Mrs Poulteney, their freedoms as well . . . I do not fully control these creatures of my mind . . .

(Chapter 13)

Despite the presence of the omniscient narrator, the novel maintains the stance of a First Person account, not a First Person who is part of the action but one who is part of 'the illusion' ('Notes', p. 142); thus, in Chapter 55, at least one of the narrators is fleshed out, 'a massively bearded face . . . a man of forty or so', rather like, in fact, the bearded figure of John Fowles himself, who was forty-one in the year he wrote the novel. This narrator sits in Charles's first-class compartment on his railway journey to London and asks '. . . what the devil am I going to do with you?' Ultimately he decides not to decide but to give his reader two possible versions of the ending, both

---

*It may not be perverse to compare this 'local spy' with Wordsworth's narrator in 'The Thorn', a poem which has a number of similarities with *The French Lieutenant's Woman*.

†'Notes on an Unfinished Novel' in *The Novel Today*, ed. Malcolm Bradbury, Fontana/ Collins, Glasgow, 1977, p. 144. Henceforth referred to as 'Notes'.

dependent on the same plot, and allow him to choose between them, a technical trick which could belong only to a novel of our own century.

The reappearance of this enigmatic figure, or a figure rather like him, in Chapter 61, heralds the offering of an alternative ending; if he has presided over the first and Victorian ending he removes himself from the second, twentieth-century ending, apparently leaving the characters to choose for themselves; yet an 'I' is still there to address the reader, to philosophise as Charles walks away from Sarah and from love.

In the form of his narration and his choice of narrators Fowles was obeying his own edict, written down in a memorandum to himself:

> Remember the etymology of the word. A novel is something new. It must have relevance to the writer's now – so don't ever pretend you live in 1867; or make sure the reader knows it's a pretence.
>
> ('Notes', p. 138)

His method of dealing with plot and narration is the 'something new' in his novel, the relevance to his own 'now' which had to embrace not only his own knowledge of the novel form as it has evolved over two and a half centuries, but also his knowledge of Alain Robbe-Grillet and the *nouveau roman*.

By creating a multiplicity of narrators, Fowles has availed himself of the omniscience of the Victorians whilst at the same time reserving a freedom of action and expression for his characters which modernist writers see as paramount. Unlike many twentieth-century novelists he refuses to reject the form of nineteenth-century narration:

> I've always liked the ironic voice that the line of great nineteenth-century novelists, from Austen through to Conrad, all used so naturally. We tend today to remember the failures of that tone . . . rather than its virtues . . .
>
> ('Notes', p. 141)

He is, too, aware of the hypocrisy in the stance of the *nouveau roman* writers, who insist that the presence of the writer comes between characters and readers and must therefore be expunged from the text: 'Nothing can get us off the charge of omnipotence', he maintains ('Notes', p. 143). Thus, he makes use of two opposing modes of narration, fusing them into a technically original, compelling and brilliant novel.

Apart from the question of the identity of the narrator, Fowles uses many more conventional and traditional narrative devices in the novel. In some ways we might see the story as beginning *in medias res* (in the middle of things), since much of what is significant to the plot has already occurred when we first meet the principal characters. The simple retelling of the salient facts about the background of two of the main characters takes place in Chapter 3 (Charles), and 5 and 11 (Ernestina). Something is told about Sarah in Chapter 9, but by then we have already learned much of her story in Chapters 2 and 6; the alert reader, however, should notice the difference in the telling of these various accounts: an omniscient narrator is responsible for informing us about the lives of Charles and Ernestina and for the comments on Sarah in Chapter 9, whilst our earlier information about Sarah 'is all gossip' (Chapter 2), told first by Ernestina to Charles and then by Mr Forsythe, the Vicar, to Mrs Poulteney. These different modes of narration become significant when we learn, much later in the novel, that the stories that have circulated in Lyme about Sarah are untrue. We have been misled, however, not by the narrator, but by the gossips of Lyme Regis and, indeed, by Sarah herself who has acquiesced in the rumours. In Chapter 47, when Charles realises that he 'had forced a virgin', not only his but also our whole assessment of Sarah has to be revised.

The plot of the novel is never straightforward, however; the novelist constantly plays with time in one way or another to achieve a maximum effect. Parallel events are shown sequentially, so that the impact of one is heightened by the superimposing of another; thus, Charles's first direct encounter alone with Sarah occurs in Chapters 10 and 12, whilst in between, in Chapter 11, we are shown Ernestina languishing restless and unwell in her bed in Aunt Tranter's house. However, in Chapter 12, the return of Charles to Mrs Tranter's and his deliberate conceal-ment of his meeting with Sarah, accidental though it was, is paralleled with Sarah's return to Mrs Poulteney's house and the accusation of sin against her because she has been walking on Ware Commons. She too conceals her meeting: 'No one frequents it. That is why I go there – to be alone.' Thus an evasion of the truth in accounts immediately following each other in the same chapter strengthens the connection between Charles and Sarah in the reader's mind.

At other times events are presented in reverse order; for instance, though we learn from Ernestina's comments in Chapter 24 of Charles's uncle's intention to marry Mrs Tomkins, the actual account of the interview in which Charles himself learns of it does not occur until Chapter 26. Interlayered with these events is the story of Sarah's dismissal from Mrs Poulteney's employment, which Charles learns about in Chapter 24 but which is presented to the reader only in Chapter 30.

The most striking example of time-devices, however, is the disloca-tion of time which occurs in Chapters 45 and 61. The events of Chapters 42, 43 and 44 are a shock to the sensibilities of a modern reader, even though they appear to end the novel in traditional style.

The extent of the shock suggests how subtly Fowles has infused the novel with twentieth-century beliefs and thoughts; it is no surprise to us to be told in Chapter 45 that the preceding neatly arranged ending is not what happened but what Charles imagined might happen. For Chapter 61 we are already prepared by the narrator's statement at the end of Chapter 55 that he intends to give two versions of Charles's story. Thus, the penultimate chapter voices our romantic hopes and the final chapter gives credence to our existential fears, more fully realised because of the possibilities held out to us in the happy ending.

Other devices used to help the narrative along, and well-tried in novels almost from the inception of the genre, are diary comments and letters, though in *The French Lieutenant's Woman* they play a minor part, the interception by Sam of Sarah and Charles's letters being more significant than the letters themselves.

The French Lieutenant's Woman and existentialism

John Fowles admits to being 'much more at home in French than in English literature' since he left Oxford ('Notes', p. 147). This inevitably led him to an interest in the theories of existentialism propounded by Jean-Paul Sartre in the 1940s. Fowles's earlier novels, *The Collector* (1963) and *The Magus* (1966), are both influenced by existentialism, and he himself claims that in *The French Lieutenant's Woman* he is 'trying to show an existential awareness before it was chronologically possible' ('Notes', p. 140), but he goes on to explain:

> . . . it has always seemed to me that the Victorian Age, especially from 1850 on, was highly existentialist in many of its personal dilemmas . . . By the 1860s the great iron structures of [Victorian] philosophies, religions, and social stratifications were already beginning to look dangerously corroded to the more perspicacious.
>
> Just such a man [i.e. one of the more perspicacious], an existentialist before his time, walks down the quay and sees that mysterious back, feminine, silent, also existentialist, turned to the horizon . . .
>
> ('Notes', pp. 140f.)

The most significant of the existential theories which seem to govern Charles and Sarah is that we exist and are entirely responsible for our own lives, that there is no god to be blamed when things go wrong. At the same time, we exist in a world with its own laws, morals and traditions, and we cannot separate ourselves from it. We cannot rely on rules of bahaviour or thought which we ourselves have codified to hold true in every situation. The context of our problems is constantly changing and every decision involves a reassessment. Existentialist *angst* ('anguish'/'anxiety' do not quite give us the sense but are the closest we can get in English) thus arises because at every point in life choices have to made; we are completely free to choose between two possibilities but, equally, the responsibility for such choices is entirely our own and cannot be shared or passed on, for we have shaped our own existence without the intervention of any supreme power. We alone, having weighed up our past actions and our future needs, can make the decisions which influence our lives and which create our own reality.

In considering the characters of Charles and Sarah in the next section, the impact of existentialism has to be borne in mind, for though they themselves precede its birth, their creator has envisaged them in an existential image.

Characters

Sarah Woodruff

Sarah is the protagonist of *The French Lieutenant's Woman*, a twentieth-century feminist born before her time. Yet she is also a typical woman of the nineteenth century, born poor, educated beyond her station, with no place in her own world. Her father was a tenant farmer in Hardy country near Beaminster. Deluded by ideas of noble ancestry he bought his own farm and when it failed he 'went quite literally mad and was sent to Dorchester Asylum' (Chapter 9). We know nothing of Sarah's mother or any other relations; after her father's death she appears to be alone in the world and she leaves Dorchester to become a governess in the family of Captain Talbot in Charmouth.

From time to time, as the novel progresses, scraps of physical description help to build up a picture of Sarah. She is not beautiful, scarcely even pretty, but there is something compelling and intriguing about her face. She has auburn hair, dark eyes, strong nose, mouth and eyebrows and a brown complexion, unfashionable in Victorian times when women prized pale skin untouched by the rays of the sun. Until the two final chapters Sarah is always seen obeying the fashion dictates of her own poverty and the expectations of the upper classes for whom she works. Her long hair is tied back severely and tucked inside her collar, and she dresses in the widow's colours of indigo and black. Yet from the outset we are aware that she is not entirely what she seems, and her conversations with Charles suggest that she has taken note of her own situation in life and has made deliberate choices to follow the path she has embarked upon. It is not, however, until the last two chapters that we see her, through Charles's eyes, as the 'New Woman' and dressed accordingly. The contrast between her first appearance and her last represents the enigma of Sarah.

It was with Sarah Woodruff that the novel began, not in Chapter 1 but back at the time when the seeds of the book first impressed themselves on John Fowles: 'A woman stands at the end of a deserted quay and stares out to sea' ('Notes', p. 136). This image he describes in the same essay as a 'mythopoeic still'. Such an image of Sarah is apt, for her loneliness is her most striking characteristic, a loneliness which she translates into a fierce desire for independence; what she desires is not so much financial independence as inviolability, an inner life, a spirit untouched by anyone around her; she displays the soul of a twentieth-century feminist in the frail body of a nineteenth-century servant who would appear to be utterly dependent.

The first part of her story, then, is all too familiar from many nineteenth-century novels. She is courted, deceived and deserted by an unscrupulous lover, Lieutenant Varguennes, a Frenchman whom she had befriended when he was shipwrecked and wounded. The reader realises only much later in the novel that Sarah, though perhaps duped by Varguennes, was not seduced by him, for she remains a virgin; the sum of his deception would appear to be in allowing her to believe he was unmarried. When we contemplate Sarah's intrigue with Charles we may even be forced to wonder whether she felt duped by Varguennes in that he did not give her a child, that his only legacy to her was to have compromised her in the eyes of the world without fulfilling her. Varguennes, too, perhaps, like Charles, was tortured by lust and desire, his marriage troubled or destroyed by his memories of Sarah. We do not know, for we do not follow his story.

We do know, however, that Sarah now finds herself violated by kindness – the gentleness and understanding of Mrs Talbot, the love of little Paul and Virginia. Such kindness intervenes between her and what she believes to be the motives for the choice she has made. She accepts the job with Mrs Poulteney because cruelty, harshness and injustice make no claims upon her. Again, she rejects Aunt Tranter's offer of help because kindness demands reciprocation. In Mrs Poulteney's household she not only achieves an independence of mind and spirit but she also finds the opportunity to make others beholden to her, for she protects and is kind to Millie and even heaps coals of fire upon Mrs Poulteney's head by remembering her birthday and embroidering an antimacassar for her.

If the desire for independence is a twentieth-century trait in Sarah's character, her desire for happiness may be seen as universal. It is expressed in her words to Charles in Chapter 60:

> I never expected to be happy in life. Yet I find myself happy where I
> am situated now . . . I am happy, I am at last arrived, or so it seems
> to me, where I belong.

The contrary demands of independence and happiness perhaps help to
explain, as far as it is possible to explain, Sarah's troubling and
enigmatic character.

Fulfilment in marriage and motherhood was a nineteenth-century
woman's dream that Sarah might have expected to achieve through
Varguennes. Fulfilment in motherhood without marriage is a
twentieth-century practical possibility which she seems to have chosen
Charles to fulfil for her. It is her misfortune that love and lust displace
the simpler requirements of happiness and independence. In Charles's
pursuit of her she discovers a sexual need she had not reckoned on, and
to this need she is willing to sacrifice her hard-won independence of
spirit, deliberately scheming to lose her job in order to throw herself on
Charles's mercy. In her pursuit of Charles which follows she makes the
further decision to fulfil herself sexually before disappearing from his
life.

The choices she makes after this point, when she exonerates Charles
from blame and takes full responsibility for her own life, show us the
existentialist spirit at work. It is the unexpected return of Charles that
upsets her calculations.

Both the solutions at the end of the novel leave Sarah with an
existential *angst*: the choice between love and happiness in a marriage
which might also, but not certainly, allow her independence, or
happiness and independence without marriage but with the possibility
of love denied her. In both cases she has to make the final choice alone:
in Chapter 60 she actively placates Charles's anger, though he is willing
to be placated; in Chapter 61 she makes less effort, but Charles does
not respond to 'her hand on his arm', except to feel that he is being
both deceived and defiled.

Thus we are finally left with a character who never fully reveals
herself, a character that we, together with the author, have perhaps
invented.

Charles

Charles's character is more consistent and less complex than Sarah's.
He is tall, handsome, of aristocratic lineage, every nineteenth-century
young woman's dream of a desirable husband. Though his father is
dead he has at the beginning of the story every expectation of
inheriting the family title and fortune from his elderly bachelor uncle.
He has had the upbringing of a gentleman; he studied classics at

Cambridge, but left without completing his degree. He then toyed with the idea of taking Holy Orders until, encouraged by his father, he settled for Sin and Travel as alternatives. He was not, however, completely persuaded to abandon his intellectual pursuits, for by the time that we meet him he has become a keen amateur scientist, with palaeontological, geological and biological interests – a dilettante scholar, perhaps, but a dedicated one nevertheless.

At the age of thirty-two he prizes his independence enough never to have allowed himself an emotional involvement with a woman of his own class. Yet, because of this he is an innocent and is easily trapped by Ernestina's scheming. By the same token he appears to have been easy prey for Sarah, if that is how we wish to see the story.

Towards the lower classes Charles displays in general the genteel manners of one born of generations of men and women at home with their own superiority. Thus, his approach to Sarah is one of kindly concern, mixed with the gallantry of a gentleman towards one of the opposite sex who appears to be in need of help. His motives also seem to be partly scientific, representing his desire to pin down and investigate a species unknown to him.

It soon becomes apparent to the reader that Charles's 'chance' meetings with Sarah in Ware Cleeves have been carefully orchestrated, first subconsciously by him and later more deliberately by her. Guile is, however, foreign to his nature; he finds himself unwittingly led into deception and emotionally incapable of explaining to Ernestina an affair that is, in fact, innocent, though from the outset more complicated than he dare admit, even to himself. He is happier and more at home in the masculine realm of intellectual discussion and argument with Dr Grogan than with the flirtatious conversation of Ernestina in Mrs Tranter's drawing-room or with the compelling intensity of Sarah in an environment where his scientific interest in fossils might have been expected to predominate.

In his original pursuit of Sarah, in his submission to her pursuit and in the final fulfilment of his lust Charles may be seen as an ordinary representative of nineteenth-century aristocracy. It is only after sexual intercourse with her that he himself fully realises his commitment to love. He abandons Ernestina, marriage and all material hopes for the future to the uncertain hope of continuing his tenuous relationship with Sarah. In this act, as the narrator comments at the end of Chapter 10, 'the whole Victorian Age was lost', for Charles behaves not as a Victorian gentleman but as a man moved by real feelings. Yet his first reaction is to seek escape from the wrong he feels he has done Sarah. In the church scene which follows (Chapter 48) he goes through a period of existential agony, repeatedly begging God's forgiveness, not only for his sins of commission in the physical world – selfishness and unchastity – but also for his sins of omission in the spiritual world, epitomised in his 'lack of faith in [God's] wisdom and charity'; but, even as he prays, he is aware of the lack of response; God is not present in his church; he does not attend to the prayer: 'it was hopeless. He knew it was not heard.'

For the man responsible for his own life forgiveness is not an option; his life and his decisions are his own. Charles thus moves forward, knowing that he alone must accept the consequences of his actions. His desertion of Ernestina, his long-drawn-out pursuit of Sarah move him towards the existential *angst* of the final chapters: to marry Sarah, to be responsible for two lives besides his own is, like the solution of Chapter 44, a romantic dream. So he finally accepts that 'life . . . is not a symbol, is not one riddle and one failure to guess it . . . but is to be, however inadequately, emptily, hopelessly . . . endured' (Chapter 61).

Ernestina

Ernestina is a typical figure from Victorian fiction. Rich, pampered, moderately pretty, empty-headed and something of a Philistine, she seeks a husband, and Charles appears to be an ideal candidate for the position. The narrator's reference to Thackeray's Becky Sharp makes it clear to us that Ernestina's wiles to catch Charles suggest a cunning in her nature; this lack of straightforwardness in her character is seen at various times throughout the novel in her teasing of Charles, and particularly when she appears to faint after he breaks off the engagement (Chapter 50).

Born into trade, heiress of one of the *nouveaux riches*, she has none of Charles's gentility and kindliness. She speaks harshly to Mrs Tranter, she is unkind to Mary and she repeats spiteful gossip about Sarah. Her plans for renovating and improving Charles's ancestral manor are completely lacking in taste, and her reactions to his probable loss of title and fortune are vulgar and shocking. In the first part of the novel the reader has little sympathy for Ernestina. She is capricious and selfish, and harbours a grudging resentment against any other woman to whom Charles behaves civilly. It is perhaps ironic that she suspects him of flirting with Mary at the very time when Sarah, whom Ernestina completely disregards, is absorbing his attention.

When Charles breaks off the engagement, Ernestina's reactions, with her threats of breach of promise, are abhorrent to our twentieth-century sensibilities. Yet it is at this moment that we begin to feel for her. Though she behaves badly, she has cause, for nothing that has gone before has prepared her for this moment. The broken engagement not only damages her self-esteem but it also makes her more aware of her real, if rather shallow, affection for Charles. Later, when her father in his anger and vindictiveness tries to destroy Charles, Ernestina shows a charity towards him that suggests she had truly loved him. Thus, we find that she has hidden reserves of character of which we become aware only at the moment when she disappears from the novel.

Mrs Poulteney and Mrs Fairley

These two women may well be treated together as, in their own stations, they are equally vile. Both may be found under various names in many Victorian novels. Mrs Poulteney's wealth and privileged position have made her believe in her own superiority and moral rightness to the exclusion of all sympathy towards others. She deliberately chooses to take on Sarah as her companion, not for Sarah's sake but in order to persuade God that she, Mrs Poulteney, can be generous towards sinners. Her unhappy household, however, is not a very good advertisement for Christian charity; it is ruled over by the mean, vicious, gossiping Mrs Fairley who, jealous of Sarah's position as companion, sets out to defame her.

The two women, mistress and housekeeper, deserve each other!

Sam Farrow

Sam Farrow shares his Christian name with Dickens's Sam Weller from *The Pickwick Papers*, and the two Sams are both 'gentlemen's gentlemen', but at that point the comparison ends. Whereas in Dickens's work Sam is a tower of strength to his master – honest, decent, faithful, extricating him from scrapes and generally acting as a loyal servant – Sam Farrow is cunning, dishonest, self-seeking, untrustworthy, entirely lacking the endearing qualities of his predecessor. The comparison, however, perhaps helps to underline Charles's essential naïvety; though apparently a man of the world, like Mr Pickwick he lacks experience in judging the characters of those less honest and decent than he; thus he is easy prey to the womanly wiles, first of Ernestina and then of Sarah; this is made more apparent to us when we realise that he is completely oblivious to his servant's perfidy. Sam traps him and betrays him; he steals not only Charles's letters but also the expensive brooch that was sent to Sarah. His actions lead to Charles's utter desolation for, without Sam's intervention, Charles might well have salvaged something from the ruins of his life and the possibilities hinted at in the penultimate chapter might have become the realities of the finale.

In a novel in which Victorian times are shown in relation to the twentieth century, Sam Farrow represents to some extent the new breed of independent servants that had grown up since Sam Weller's time; simultaneously, Fowles's presentation of him helps to show us that emancipation among the lower classes was man's domain, for the women lack the opportunities for independence that he has.

Sam's one redeeming quality is his love for Mary which, from the outset, appears to be far stronger than Charles's love for Ernestina. Nevertheless, we are aware that it is not entirely selfless and that he throws up his job with Charles only in the hope of getting something better. By the time his feelings of guilt persuade him to give a helping hand to his ex-master, it is really too late.

Dr Grogan

Dr Grogan is not an unusual character in Victorian novels; his disinterested attitude towards learning is common among fictional doctors of the time. He is able to engage Charles in intellectual discussion upon contemporary scientific matters; he has a considerable store of abstruse knowledge about esoteric branches of medicine, yet he chooses to work as a doctor in a small town such as Lyme, supplying the medical needs of a simple community.

Though he has advanced ideas, however, and though he enjoys Charles's company, he proves to be a typical Victorian in his responses first to Sarah, whom he wants to incarcerate in an asylum, and, second, to the broken engagement in which affair he sides entirely with Ernestina.

References and allusions

Reading *The French Lieutenant's Woman* is a little like browsing in a library: all sorts of literary and intellectual treasures are laid out before us for our delectation, and we often feel that each one opens out for us tempting new vistas which we must investigate at our leisure. Every one of the sixty-one chapters has at least one, and frequently two, apposite epigraphs, taken mainly, though not exclusively, from nineteenth-century literature – poems, novels, scientific, political and sociological prose.

By far the greatest number of these epigraphs are from literary sources and almost a quarter of them are from Tennyson. Their purpose is primarily to set the tone for the chapter which follows. The first chapter is thus preceded by a quotation from Thomas Hardy's poem 'The Riddle' and establishes the mystery, the mythic quality of Sarah, who is introduced to us looking out over the sea in exactly the same fashion as the woman in the poem. Whilst the scientific, sociological and political epigraphs are generally chosen in order to extend our understanding of the background to the novel, the literary ones are designed to prepare our emotional reactions. A knowledge of Tennyson's 'Maud' and *In Memoriam* and of certain of the poems of Arnold, Clough and Hardy will help to reinforce the sense of sadness, loss and desire which pervades the book. Certainly the epigraphs are significant in the context of the chapters they precede and should be considered as an integral part of the whole. Fowles himself occasionally draws attention to the relevance of the epigraphs (see, for instance, his footnote in Chapter 5 or his comment in the penultimate paragraph of the novel).

Most of the authors from whom Fowles quotes make some kind of appearance in the novel itself. The story is set in Hardy country and in Chapter 35 Fowles refers to being 'under the shadow, the very relevant shadow, of the great novelist who towers over this part of England of which I write'. Hardy's shadow is certainly present in *The French Lieutenant's Woman* in the discussion of the position of women, in the comments upon sex and in many of the ideas presented in the novel. A number of the characters, too, are in some ways reminiscent of Hardy. Sarah, without her existentialist characteristics, can be seen as a Hardyesque figure, educated to rise above the class she was born into and thus unable to find her place in life. Her father, like Tess's father in *Tess of the D'Urbervilles* (1891), has delusions of ancestral grandeur, whilst Charles, like Angel Clare in the same novel, finds himself able to condone his own sin but condemns what he believes to be the same sin in Sarah.

Among other nineteenth-century novelists Fowles owes a debt also to Jane Austen and to Charles Dickens and makes allusions to several others, including Thackeray and George Eliot. Just as the novel is set in Hardy country in general, so its specific setting in Lyme Regis recalls Austen's *Persuasion*, and the romantic Ernestina points out to Charles as they walk along the Cobb, 'These are the very steps that Jane Austen made Louisa Musgrove fall down in *Persuasion*' (Chapter 2). But *Persuasion* is a true nineteenth-century novel, and despite the frustrations of love which occur it ends romantically with Anne marrying her Frederick. At the same time, we might observe that in that novel a scheming Mrs Tomkins, in the guise of the widow Mrs Clay, marries the heir to Kellynch Hall. Whilst Hardy and Austen are used and imitated, Dickens's Sam Weller is contrasted strongly with the disloyal, vain, idle Sam Farrow who serves Charles as valet, and, in case we should miss the contrast, Fowles draws attention to it in Chapter 7.

Poetry too serves to extend our imaginative horizons and to evoke emotional responses made more poignant by poetic language. The use of Tennyson's 'Maud' in many of the epigraphs creates an atmosphere of regret and of undefined loss; the anguished protagonist of that poem, like Charles, seeks reconciliation and harmony with the woman he loves and, like Charles, suffers her ultimate loss. Equally moving is the subtle use made of Matthew Arnold's 'To Marguerite' at the very end of the novel, recalling to our mind Charles's wanderings in Chapter 58 where the poem is quoted in its entirety. It is a poem of loneliness, of isolation, which holds out no hope of experience shared:

> Yes: in the sea of life enisl'd,
> With echoing straits between us thrown,
> Dotting the shoreless watery wild,
> We mortal millions live *alone*.

It embodies the existentialist philosophical belief that each is responsible for his own destiny; it ends, like the novel, with the 'unplumb'd, salt, estranging sea', and the brief echo of this phrase suggests to us an unsatisfied Charles, eternally wandering.

Rich as it is in literary references and allusions, *The French Lieutenant's Woman* also makes use of the work of Lyell and Darwin, not only with reference to Charles's scientific interests, but also because their work is symptomatic of a changing world. The theory of evolution is reinforced by the fossils embedded in the stone of the Cobb which Charles and Ernestina walk upon and by the tests which he and Sarah find in the woods on Ware Cleeves. It is also apparent in the whole fabric of nineteenth-century society: Mr Freeman with his wealth and influence has accepted the principles of evolution in society, even if he rejects their wider implications. When in Chapter 37 he declares to Charles that 'You will never get me to agree that we are all descended from monkeys', he nevertheless goes on to exploit the theory of evolution for his own ends, pointing out to Charles that man must adapt himself to his environment in order to survive and that Charles must face such adaptation in his own life. Thus, through comparison with scientific theories, we are shown an evolving society in which the aristocracy must earn their own living and in which women must eventually find independence.

A seminal work, which Fowles himself recommends 'most warmly' in his 'Acknowledgments' to the novel is *Human Documents of the Victorian Age* by E. Royston Pike (1967). Not only are a number of the epigraphs from this book, but also with its help the whole atmosphere of Victorian England is recreated in *The French Lieutenant's Woman* – not the spurious aura of wealth, prosperity and uprightness, but rather the genuine variety of life. Wealth and influence are seen existing side by side with sordid misery, men and women of the leisured classes in close conjunction with the overworked, ill-treated and exploited.

It has only been possible here to make the briefest of references to all the background reading necessary for a full understanding of *The French Lieutenant's Woman*, but this short section is intended to help readers to follow up some of it in greater detail for themselves.

Style and language

The style of *The French Lieutenant's Woman* in many ways resembles the novel it sets out to pose as. The friendly, familiar tone of the narrator conversing with his readers prevents us from being overawed by the erudition which pervades the book. Nevertheless, the novelist himself is clearly at home in French and Latin as well as in English, is well-informed about geology and palaeontology, the Darwinian theory of evolution and nineteenth-century responses to it, psychiatry, history, literature and many other branches of knowledge. All these are introduced into the novel, sometimes in a matter-of-fact way through which they become entirely integrated into the story, some-times as deliberate interpolations or digressions, such as the account of the trial of Emile de La Roncière and the long quotation from *Observations Medico-psychologiques* which take up most of Chapter 28. It is scarcely possible to read, understand and enjoy *The French Lieutenant's Woman* without a smattering of knowledge in several of these disciplines, though the lack of detailed knowledge is probably not a serious drawback.

The novel is a mixture of straightforward prose, interspersed with dialogue. Despite Fowles's qualms about whether the nineteenth-century conversations are realistic and convincing (see 'Notes', p. 139), he seems to have hit the right note, for the dialogue, if stilted to twentieth-century ears, is exactly how we imagine nineteenth-century people – at least nineteenth-century characters in novels – to have spoken.

With all the devices already referred to – the allusions, references, quotations, and so on – there are a few literary devices still to be observed. For a novel so firmly placed in rural surroundings and beside the sea, it is perhaps fitting that much of the language – imagery, similes, metaphors – is taken from nature. A good number of the literary epigraphs embody such language, and the most persistent imagery is that of animals and birds, particularly of the preying and the preyed upon. It is first introduced through the description of Charles in Chapter 3 when we see him unwillingly joining in the sport of shooting pheasants and partridges and 'adamantly refus[ing] to hunt the fox'. When the following chapter describes Mrs Poulteney's 'eagle eye', compares her with a 'plump vulture' and tells of the man-traps she sets in her garden, the undercurrent of animal imagery begins to become apparent, an imagery that graphically and economically adds to our understanding of character. Mrs Poulteney is at various other times 'a bulldog about to sink its teeth into a burglar's ankles' (Chapter 9) and 'an infuriated black swan' (Chapter 19), whilst her housekeeper, Mrs Fairley, is 'a weasel' (Chapter 9). At Mrs Poulteney's imagined death and damnation, which occurs in the false ending in Chapter 44, she falls 'like a shot crow', thus being shown as impotent herself to do evil but also as a warning to others. When Charles, obeying society's demands at Lyme, is required to make social visits with Ernestina and her aunt, he is seen in Mrs Poulteney's house as 'a plump mouse dropping between the claws of a hungry cat' (Chapter 14), though later, just before he embraces Sarah in the barn, we are invited to see him as a 'tiger' (Chapter 31).

A number of other images reinforce those of preying, of cruelty, of captivity. Again, many of them refer to Mrs Poulteney: she is an 'ogress' (Chapter 9), a 'pagan idol . . . oblivious of the blood sacrifice her pitiless stone face demanded' (Chapter 12); in Chapter 4 it is suggested that she could have been a member of the Gestapo; Marlborough House is a tomb from which the goldfinch Mary gains her liberty (Chapter 11) and 'barred surroundings' encaging Sarah (Chapter 14). The vocabulary, too, throughout the novel, is rich in words of judgment, punishment, suffering and similar ideas.

If the animal imagery is used in general to depict the harshness of nature and of mankind, flowers and plants suggest something kindlier. In Chapter 10 the wood above the shoreline is described picturesquely with

> . . . its wild arbutus and ilex and other trees rarely seen growing in England; its enormous ashes and beeches; its green Brazilian chasms choked with ivy and the liana of wild clematis; its bracken that grows seven, eight feet tall; its flowers that bloom a month earlier than anywhere else in the district.

It is in this 'English Garden of Eden', Ware Commons, that Charles meets with Sarah Woodruff, and his first visit here is presented in idyllic terms:

> The ground about him was studded gold and pale yellow with celandines and primroses and banked by the bridal white of densely blossoming sloe; where jubilantly green-tipped elders shaded the mossy banks of the little brook he had drunk from were clusters of moschatel and woodsorrel, most delicate of English spring flowers. Higher up the slope he saw the white heads of anemones, and beyond them deep green drifts of bluebell leaves . . .

Amidst this rich, burgeoning fertility he finds Sarah asleep. The paradisial connotations of the scene hold within them both the innocence and the sin of Adam and Eve. The whole description of the lush and wayward beauty of the surroundings is in striking contrast to Charles's order to Sam in Chapter 8, before he enters this 'Garden of Eden', to 'buy what flowers he could' and take them to Ernestina, as it is also to the 'fountain of spring flowers' which Sam delivers in Chapter 11, a bouquet already reduced to order by Mary and placed in a vase which Ernestina insists should be moved away from her bedside to the dressing table. The wild and passionate disorder of the first scene is symbolic of the emotions which Sarah arouses in Charles, whilst the cut flowers placed at a distance from Ernestina symbolise the relationship between him and his fiancée.

When, much later in the plot, Charles goes to find Sarah after she has been dismissed by Mrs Poulteney, the descriptions of birds and flowers are again rich and abundant, but now he recognises them as a threat to the even tenor of his life, calling him to abandon the cloying restrictions of convention:

> Some paranoiac transference of guilt now made him feel that the trees, the flowers, even the inanimate things around him were watching him. Flowers became eyes, stones had ears, the trunks of the reproving trees were a numberless Greek chorus.
>
> (Chapter 29)

The threat is realised when, two chapters further on, Charles finds himself taking Sarah into his arms and kissing her passionately. However, the moment of understanding, the knowledge that he acquires, are sufficient to banish him from Eden; the 'tired stems of narcissus in a Toby jug on the mantelpiece' (Chapter 46) in Sarah's room in Endicott's Family Hotel should warn the reader that Sarah, like Ernestina, has succumbed to order and planning, is in control of a situation which can now get out of hand only for Charles – as indeed it does.

When Charles leaves her after their brief love-making and enters the church to pray, his choice of life is put starkly before him:

> You stay in prison, what your time calls duty, honour, self-respect, and you are comfortably safe. Or you are free and crucified. Your only companions the stones, the thorns . . .
>
> (Chapter 48)

The Garden of Eden has led, as apparently it always must, to the Garden of Gethsemane and the Crucifixion. Charles's alternatives are the safety of a place in the restrictive society of Victorian Britain as husband of Ernestina, as director of Freeman's, as a tame dilettante scholar but without love, or the life of an outcast from society, punished, despised, abandoned by family and friends but accompanied by Sarah and by love in 'Paris . . . Florence . . . Rome'.

Despite his choice of Sarah, however, the abandonment to liberty eludes him and he finds only crucifixion. His dream of 'some jasmine-scented room' where he and Sarah 'would lie awake, in each other's arms, infinitely alone' (Chapter 54) ends in the wisteria-covered house in Cheyne Walk where Sarah has found her own liberty, a liberty which cannot include Charles – unless, of course, we ourselves choose to accept the romantic ending to Chapter 60 . . .

Running parallel to the nature imagery is that of colour, green being the dominant image of the life-force which seems to pass from one female character in the novel to another. It is, at first, with Ernestina, walking on the Cobb dressed in her 'rich green coat', in contrast to the black clothes in which we see Sarah dressed (Chapter 1). It passes to Mary when, in Chapter 15, Ernestina gives her her 'green walking dress' to try to make amends to Charles and her aunt for the unpleasantness which occurs during the visit to Mrs Poulteney; certainly if we see it as a sign of fecundity we know that Mary becomes pregnant soon after she receives this gift. Finally it passes to Sarah; when Charles visits her in Endicott's Family Hotel the sombre colours in which he has always seen her have been exchanged for something more colourful. She has a red Welsh blanket over her legs, and the green merino shawl which she had bought is thrown loosely over her shoulders, allowing Charles to see that beneath it she is dressed in her nightgown; furthermore, her hair, no longer restrained, falls, we are told, 'over her green shoulders' (Chapter 46). The moment of intercourse which follows results, as we know from Chapter 60, in the conception of Lalage.

When we next see Sarah, in the Rossetti house in Cheyne Walk, though she is colourfully dressed in what Charles recognises as 'the full uniform of the New Woman' she has abandoned the green of the life-force, a fact which perhaps points to the ending of the final chapter as the one we must accept.

Part 4
Hints for study

The French Lieutenant's Woman is a complicated and difficult novel, and no summary can hope to do justice to the ramifications of the text. There is no substitute for reading the novel itself. When you have read it through, taken in the story and received a general impression of the book, read it again more slowly, giving special attention to particular aspects of the novel. On your second reading take notes and jot down quotations; make sure that your note or quotation is followed by a bracketed page number (or chapter number if you are not using your own book and may have to use a different edition on a subsequent reading). What ought you to be looking for when you study the novel more closely? Perhaps you should consider at least some of the following:

(1) setting
(2) characters
(3) narrative technique
(4) point of view
(5) style and language
(6) allusions and references
(7) nineteenth-century aspects
(8) twentieth-century aspects

Can you think of other interesting or significant aspects of the novel which you could add to this list? (Part 3 of these Notes may help you.)

Always remember to return to the text in order to support or illustrate points you are making. Critics may suggest ideas to you, but you should ensure that you accept these ideas only if your own knowledge of the novel confirms them. A critic can be wrong; or two critics may disagree. Even if you believe a critic to be right, check that the text does support his argument. Try to find quotations other than those he has used which could have been used on his side; are there other passages in the novel which appear to refute his arguments? When you were reading Part 3 of these Notes did you agree with everything that was stated? If so, did you try to think of other quotations that supported what was said? If you disagreed, are you able to illustrate your own beliefs by reference to the text?

Because John Fowles assumes in his reader a knowledge of

nineteenth-century novels it will help you to read one or two. He sets the story in Lyme where some scenes from Jane Austen's *Persuasion* (1818) take place, so why not start by reading that novel? At least some of the ingredients of *The French Lieutenant's Woman* are to be found in Austen's novel; most obvious is the romantic ending in which love triumphs, and Anne and Frederick Wentworth marry after the frustrations of disappointed love are resolved. This can be compared with the ending contained in the penultimate chapter of *The French Lieutenant's Woman*. List some of the other similarities or differences you can find. Read also Charlotte Brontë's *Jane Eyre* (1847) which will show you something of the kind of life that Sarah might have been expected to lead as a governess or companion; again, it is a novel in which love triumphs and the heroine marries the rich man. Thomas Hardy is one of Fowles's favourite nineteenth-century novelists, and *The French Lieutenant's Woman* recalls Hardy's novels in various ways, so read one of his novels. If you want to make comparisons between Sam and Dickens's Sam Weller, read *The Pickwick Papers* (1837) to which Fowles refers in Chapter 7. Finally, to help you in your understanding of the different approach of the twentieth-century novelist, read, say, D. H. Lawrence's *Sons and Lovers* and compare its ending with the ending of *Persuasion* and with the two endings of Fowles's novel. It is much more useful to read some of these books than to read criticisms of *The French Lieutenant's Woman* itself, since without this kind of background reading you will fail to see the significance of Fowles's dual story and you will probably also have difficulty in understanding any criticism of the book. Now you should be ready to examine both the Victorian and the twentieth-century aspects of the novel, again making notes and jotting down quotations.

A good way of getting to know a novel well is by looking at a particular major incident and seeing how it bears on theme, plot, character and other aspects of the book. In examining one incident you are forced to examine a number of other incidents as well. Let us take as an example the episode in Chapter 14 when Mrs Tranter, together with Ernestina and Charles, make their courtesy visit to Mrs Poulteney. The three protagonists are present, Ernestina and Charles appearing in their role as an engaged couple, and Sarah in the guise of companion to Mrs Poulteney. The three have not appeared together since the opening chapters when Sarah was completely unknown to Charles. Now Charles has met her but has concealed the fact from Ernestina and her aunt; it is a deceit that he continues to practise as the book proceeds. We should observe, too, that Sarah accepts the deceit, 'her eyes studiously avoid[ing] his', this mutual deception already at this early stage in the novel suggesting a complicity between the two, even if undesigned.

We find, too, that although we are allowed to enter into the thoughts of both Ernestina and Charles we are merely outside observers of Sarah; she maintains an air of mystery which neither we nor the other characters are able to penetrate. This takes us back to the end of Chapter 1 when she was first introduced to us as 'more like . . . a figure from myth, than any proper fragment of the petty provincial day'.

We have already seen the harshness and hypocrisy of Mrs Poulteney (see, for instance, Chapters 4, 9, 11, 12) and shall often see them again; likewise, the gentle kindliness of Mrs Tranter has persuaded us of the rightness of the narrator's comment in Chapter 5, 'Nobody could dislike Aunt Tranter'. The conversation about Mary in the incident under discussion recalls to us Mary's dismissal from Mrs Poulteney's service for allowing the stable-boy to kiss her; it also recalls Chapter 7 and Sam's distress at Mary's mockery of him and points forward to the marriage of Mary and Sam. Charles's chivalry towards women is highlighted here. Find some other examples and list them for yourself.

The duality of the narration is made apparent in the first sentence of Chapter 14, the words 'in the nineteenth century' implying that the telling of the story does not belong to that era; there are, too, other signs in this chapter that the novel is presented through twentieth-century eyes, for instance the 'computer' in Sarah's heart or the use of the word 'Nazi'. Look through the novel and find other examples of word-usage that bring the story into our own century.

Finally, notice the animal imagery used here; as we have seen in Part 3 of these Notes, Mrs Poulteney is not infrequently associated with animals and birds of prey; she sets man-traps in her garden and is described in Chapter 4 as a 'plump vulture', whilst in the chapter under consideration Sarah is a 'wild animal' and Charles a 'mouse'. Again, find for yourself other examples of such usages.

By now you have probably collected enough material to write an essay entitled 'Discuss the social visit to Mrs Poulteney and illustrate its relevance to the book as a whole'. Take care not to re-tell the story!

Suggested tasks and questions

Here are a number of tasks to perform, followed by more questions to consider and model answers to three of them:

(1) Pick out the names of five nineteenth-century literary figures from the epigraphs or from the text; write a few factual sentences about them and their work.

(2) Try to find out as much as you can about Darwin's theory of evolution and write something about it; what is its relevance to *The French Lieutenant's Woman?*

(3) Who were the Pre-Raphaelites? Several of them are mentioned in the novel by name, or by implication, as living in the house at Cheyne Walk; can you work out which ones they are?

(4) Look at a map of England and find Lyme Regis and Exeter on it.

(5) Read Jane Austen's *Persuasion* and discuss its relevance to *The French Lieutenant's Woman*.

(6) Read Tennyson's 'Maud' and show how Fowles uses it to add poignancy to his story.

(7) What is the significance to the novel of Matthew Arnold's poem 'To Marguerite'?

(8) To what extent does Chapter 1 prepare us for the story which is to follow?

(9) Discuss the character of one of the following: (a) Sarah Woodruff; (b) Charles Smithson; (c) Ernestina Freeman; (d) Dr Grogan

(10) Outline the three different endings to the novel and consider in what ways each is appropriate.

(11) Consider the suitability of the marriage planned between Charles and Ernestina.

(12) What contribution to the novel is made by the plot centring on Sam and Mary?

(13) Examine the presentation of the narrator as character.

(14) Examine the incident in Chapter 50 when Charles breaks off his engagement to Ernestina.

Model answers

(1) Pick out the names of five nineteenth-century literary figures from the epigraphs or from the text; write a few factual sentences about them and their work.

1. Thomas Hardy (1840–1928) was a poet and a novelist. He was born in Dorset, and most of his work is set in and around that part of Britain. Between 1871 and 1896 he published fourteen novels, the most controversial being the last two, *Tess of the D'Urbervilles* and *Jude the Obscure*. His best poetry was written after the death of his first wife in 1912 and appeared in the two volumes *Satires of Circumstance* (1914) and *Moments of Vision* (1917).

2. Jane Austen (1775–1817) was a novelist whose five completed novels were all published in the second decade of the nineteenth century. She was born in Hampshire and lived in various towns in the south and west of England. Her second and best-known novel, *Pride*

and Prejudice, was published in 1813 and *Persuasion*, part of which is set in Lyme, was published posthumously in 1818.

3. Mrs Caroline Norton (1808–77), a granddaughter of the playwright Richard Brinsley Sheridan, was a poet and novelist. After separation from her husband, the Hon. George Norton, she supported herself and her three sons by her writing, such as the sentimental verse story *The Lady of La Garaye*, which Sarah reads to Charles. She was one of the early feminists who helped to improve the lot and status of women in the nineteenth century.

4. Charles Dickens (1812–70) was a novelist; he was born in the south of England near Portsmouth. When he was about ten years old his father was imprisoned for debt, and the boy left school and was sent to work in a blacking factory; he later used these childhood experiences in his novels. *Pickwick Papers*, the book which features the manservant Sam Weller, was published in 1837.

5. A. H. Clough (1819–61) was a poet. He was born in Liverpool but his family emigrated to America soon after; however, Clough was sent back to England to be educated. He was elected to a fellowship at Oxford but resigned in 1848 for religious reasons. His long poem, 'The Bothie of Tober-na-Vuolich' (1848), from which one of the epigraphs for Chapter 16 is taken, is relevant to the plot of *The French Lieutenant's Woman*, for it is a romantic story in which a rich, educated young man marries a poor country girl.

---

(9) Discuss the character of: (c) Ernestina Freeman.

The novel begins with three people – the triangle of a man and two women: Charles, Ernestina and Sarah. Of the two women Ernestina appears to be the favoured one; rich and pampered, she is engaged to the aristocratic Charles Smithson. Her father is very wealthy and she is his only child. Consequently, throughout her life she has been spoiled and mollycoddled:

> Since birth her slightest cough would bring doctors; since puberty her slightest whim summoned decorators and dressmakers; and always her slightest frown caused her mama and papa secret hours of self-recrimination.

(Chapter 5)

Despite this, she suffers under a major disadvantage: her father wanted a son to carry on his business. This desire is shown in her name which is merely a feminine form of a boy's name. Ernestina herself is loved and cosseted but is seen by her father as a poor substitute for the brother who never appeared: 'I count myself a fortunate man in every respect. Except one . . .', Mr Freeman explains to Charles, 'I have no son' (Chapter 37).

Ernestina is pretty in a pert way; she has, the narrator explains, 'exactly the right face for her age . . . small-chinned, oval, delicate as a violet . . . grey eyes' (Chapter 5). This description, however, is followed by a comparison with Becky Sharp from Thackeray's *Vanity Fair*, a young lady notorious for her scheming and cunning; such an unflattering comparison, though briefly made, should put us on our guard against Ernestina. Yet we first see Ernestina rebelling against the restrictions of her age; fashionably dressed, wearing bright colours – a green coat and a magenta skirt – she is following the 'revolt against the crinoline and the large bonnet' (Chapter 1).

She is attracted to Charles partly through her sense of competition; she first meets him at a house where he has been invited in the hope that he will be interested in one of the daughters. It is Ernestina, however, who gains his attention; she clearly schemes to captivate him, teasing him, mocking him and at the same time making sure that she does not 'overplay her hand' (Chapter 11). After Charles has been vetted and approved by her parents, she continues to tease, to sulk, to act the helpless and useless young lady and perhaps finally, though too late, she comes to love him. During the scene in which he breaks the engagement she is touching, pathetic and vulgar by turns; we remember the earlier scene when he told her of his uncle's intending marriage and are inclined to react against her threat of legal action without offering her the sympathy and pity which are her due.

Ernestina is presented to us as a member of the Victorian *nouveaux riches*, but because of the form of the book we judge her by twentieth-century standards, and she is found wanting. Her philistine attitudes, her cunning, her selfishness, her lack of sympathy with Aunt Tranter and her superior manner towards servants and members of the lower classes prevent us from seeing her in any way as a tragic heroine of romance.

---

(11) Consider the suitability of the marriage planned between Charles and Ernestina

---

To the outward eye Charles and Ernestina are well matched. They are introduced to us in the first chapter, both dressed in the height of fashion, though they are walking along the blustery quay at Lyme on a late March day. It is easy for an observer to deduce that they are strangers to life in the sleepy seaside town; Ernestina, in particular, is dressed as no local lady would have dared to dress at that time, though in London she would have passed without remark.

Despite their seeming outward similarity, the backgrounds of the two young people are very different. Charles is an aristocrat, a gentleman, son of a younger son of a baronet; his prospects appear to be good, since his father's elder brother, the present baronet, remains unmarried, and the title, together with his uncle's fortune, will thus devolve upon Charles at his uncle's death. Ernestina, on the other hand, has been born into trade; yet she is the sole heiress of an immensely rich father who, having no male heir, is anxious to leave his affairs in the hands of a capable man who will inherit his business through marriage with his daughter.

By Victorian standards, therefore, marriage between Charles and Ernestina would seem to be eminently suitable. By it Charles will acquire a considerable fortune which will help to keep the house of Smithson affluent; at the same time, Ernestina will receive a title, her father will be compensated for the lack of a male heir and the children of the marriage will inherit both an aristocratic title and the fortune of a *nouveau riche* grandfather.

Yet suitable though the marriage may appear, there would have been qualms on the part of the two participants. Ernestina sees as 'the greatest obstacle' to their engagement the fact that 'her grandfather had been a draper, and Charles's had been a baronet' (Chapter 2). It is not this apparent incompatability between the two, however, but the change in Charles's circumstances that makes the match less suitable in Victorian eyes. When Charles learns of his uncle's intending marriage he realises that his part of the original bargain is at risk: not only can he no longer be sure of offering his wife a title but he will also bring little wealth into the marriage; thus all the advantages would appear to be on his side and he would feel that he had been 'morally blackmailed into a partnership' (Chapter 38).

Contradictorily, it is at this point that the reader begins to consider the Victorian marriage as not merely one of convenience. On Ernestina's side, at least, love seems to have entered into it, for she makes it clear to her doting father that she wants to marry Charles with or without the title and fortune. Later, when Charles breaks off the engagement, her anger, disappointment, jealousy and bitterness betoken love of the sort she is capable of, and it is she who saves Charles from being dragged through the courts by her father.

Looked at from a twentieth-century perspective, the marriage appears to be considerably less suitable. Charles, though indolent, has inherited an intellectual capacity as well as a particular interest in geology from his grandfather. His dilettante interest in science, in Darwinism and in the advanced ideas of his time, his inborn appreciation of art and culture render him unfit for a life of drawing-room conversation and gossip. Ernestina is eleven years his junior; the spoiled daughter of a rich father, she is used to having her own way and is unwilling to admit of anything worthwhile in Charles's more serious pursuits. Above all, Charles does not really love her, as he is forced to admit to himself in the church in Exeter after his intercourse with Sarah; looking into the future he sees that Ernestina will know that 'she is not truly loved. She is deceived. Not once, but again and again, each day of marriage' (Chapter 48).

We may thus see that the original contract between Charles and Ernestina would have made a suitable Victorian marriage and that even in 1967 when the novel was written it would not have been the least hopeful of liaisons, though it would have been a marriage of convenience rather than of passion.

Part 5

Suggestions for further reading

The text

FOWLES, JOHN: *The French Lieutenant's Woman*, Jonathan Cape Ltd, London, 1969; Little, Brown &·Co., Boston, Mass., 1969.

Background reading

ARNOLD, MATTHEW: *Poems*, Penguin Books, Harmondsworth, 1985; see particularly 'To Marguerite'.

AUSTEN, JANE: *Persuasion*, Penguin Books, Harmondsworth, 1965.

DICKENS, CHARLES: *Pickwick Papers*, Penguin Books, Harmondsworth, 1972.

FOWLES, JOHN: 'Notes on an Unfinished Novel' in *The Novel Today*, ed. Malcolm Bradbury, Fontana/Collins, Glasgow, 1977.

HARDY, THOMAS: *Tess of the D'Urbervilles*, Macmillan, London, 1975.

LAWRENCE, D. H.: *Sons and Lovers*, Penguin Books, Harmondsworth, 1948.

PIKE, E. ROYSTON: *Human Documents of the Victorian Golden Age*, George Allen & Unwin Ltd, London, 1967.

TENNYSON, ALFRED, LORD: *In Memoriam, with Maud and Other Poems*, Everyman's Library, Dent, London, 1975.

Critical studies

BRADBURY, MALCOLM: *Possibilities*, Oxford University Press, London, 1973. See Chapter XVI for a discussion of the narrator(s).

HUFFAKER, ROBERT: *John Fowles*, Twayne Publishers, Boston, Mass., 1980. See Chapter 4 which offers a fairly straightforward commentary on the text.

OLSHEN, BARRY N. and TONI, A.: *John Fowles: A Reference Guide*, G. K. Hall & Co., Boston, Mass., 1980. A useful bibliographical guide, though now getting out of date.

The author of these notes

HILDA D. SPEAR was educated at Furzedown College of Education, London, the University of London, and the University of Leicester. She has taught in various schools, colleges of education and universities, including Purdue University, Indiana. She is now a Senior Lecturer in the Department of English, the University of Dundee. Her publications include an annotated edition of *The English Poems of C. S. Calverley* (1974); *The Poems and Selected Letters of Charles Hamilton Sorley* (1978) and *Remembering, We Forget* (1979). She wrote the biographical and bibliographical section of *The Pelican Guide to English Literature V*, and she has published articles on teaching English as well as on nineteenth- and twentieth-century writers. Recently, with Abdel-Moneim Aly, she has published *Forster in Egypt* (1987). She is also the author of York Notes on *The Mayor of Casterbridge* by Thomas Hardy, *The Rainbow* by D. H. Lawrence, *Youth* and *Typhoon* by Joseph Conrad and *The Inheritors* and *The Spire* by William Golding.